Reflections on Another Life

Michael Viney

Also by Michael Viney

Another Life (1979)
Another Life Again (1981)
A Year's Turning (1998)
Ireland: A Smithsonian Natural History (2003)
Wild Mayo (2009)

Books by Ethna and Michael Viney
Eye on Nature: A Wildlife Narrative (1999)
Ireland's Ocean: A Natural History (2008)

Books by Ethna Viney
Dancing to Different Tunes: Sexuality and Its Misconceptions (1996)

Reflections on Another Life

Michael Viney

IRISH TIMES BOOKS

IRISH TIMES BOOKS
24-28 Tara Street, Dublin 2, D02CX89

First published by Irish Times Books 2015
© Michael Viney 2015
978 0 9070 1148 4

Cover photograph: Richard Johnston
Drawings: Michael Viney
Designed by PreMedia (Irish Times)

Set in Adobe Caslon Pro
Printed in Ireland by PrintRun
5 4 3 2 1
A CIP catalogue for this book is available from the British Library

Contents

Early years

Recent years

The biggest adventure
of our lives

One morning in the early years, I was pushing my bicycle up the bog road beneath Mweelrea to foot some more of our turf. It was a most unprepossessing day, cloud clinging to the mountain like fungus and an east wind pressing down from the ridge. There was nobody else in view, and as I plodded past the turf ricks I was asking myself, perhaps not unnaturally, if I was happy.

And I decided that I must be, because I wasn't looking forward to anything, and also that I had better be, because nothing much more wonderful was likely to happen. These were unfamiliar thoughts to one who had spent too much of his life longing vaguely for the evening, the weekend, the holiday, the letter in the post. Now I had no excuses, no postponement of happiness, for the future had arrived.

My wife, Ethna, and I both had good careers in the national media. In our forties, what possessed us to sell up and move west to a half-converted Land Commission cottage on a bare, thistly acre above the sea? Passing the time in the car on those endless journeys home from weekends, we can't have been so different from any other Dublin couple with a holiday house on its own patch of land and a growing disillusion with city life. But somewhere in that deadening procession through Longford, Enfield, Kilcock, Maynooth, "a pity we can't live there" became "I wonder could we?" and a list of all the things we might do once our time was our own.

Left to myself, as a closet romantic, the mere hunger for the wild and beautiful and making my days my own would not have taken me very far. But Ethna's instinct is for solving problems, for systems and making things happen. One after another, the car-borne fantasies were costed and the dreams set on schedules; that we might actually do it became, at first, rather terrifying and, then, the biggest adventure of our lives. In one surreal conclusion, Ethna drove us across to Mayo at a steady 40 kilometres per hour, with three buzzing hives in the trailer and a few loose bees trying to keep up.

1

The beekeeping bit was borrowed from her childhood on a Cavan hillside: her mother had kept hives along with turkeys and hens. From my own youth, on the outskirts of Brighton, on the Sussex shore in southern England, came a love of wild flowers and a carpenter father who, in the war years, grew food and his own tobacco, and mended our clothes and shoes. When the hole for a septic tank was being dug beside our cottage in Thallabawn, the sight of deep, loamy soil must have touched something in my genes.

In the 1970s, the idea of "alternative" living was already in full vigour. In the United States, reaction to the Vietnam War had meshed with hippiedom and the green philosophy of "deep ecology" to nourish a wave of experiment in self-sufficient rural living. In Britain, it made a guru of John Seymour, author of The Fat of the Land and Self-Sufficiency. In Ireland, the move to organic growing and the disciplined methods of permaculture (these from Australia) have led today to such projects as the Cloughjordan "ecovillage" in Co Tipperary. In 1977, these ideas were still considered eccentric, and if, as some suggested, we were "living out other people's dreams", one still had to guess what these might be.

We were never brave enough for hippiedom. (Ethna cuts my hair short, the way I like it.) And our progress towards a limited self-sufficiency met several errors of design. The currach we'd had built, for example, for the two of us to fish, scarcely felt the sea, although I kept it tarred and lashed down for many seasons in its rocky niche beyond the strand: it needed a calm day and three strong men to lift and launch it. What worked instead was a spillet – a long line of baited hooks pinned down overnight in the shallower reaches of the tide. We learned not to mind, kneeling in the wind at dawn, if all the spillet had snagged was seaweed rather than flounders and thornback ray.

On the acre, the big, costly rotavator, meant to do all the digging as it whirled away in the soil, left me deafened and exhausted, and, like the currach, it too was eventually abandoned. Instead, I learned to wield the slim, dished spade of the west, the sharpening and magical rhythm of a scythe, the lift and flick of the sléan – all for the daily mix of muscle and brain that I thought should satisfy my soul. At the kitchen window, Ethna washed, chopped, blanched and freezered as the muddy vegetables flowed in.

Our daughter, Michele, meanwhile, from eight onwards, had to cope with schoolyard suspicion of a red-headed outsider whose father might write anything in the newspaper. Our own townland was then sparsely peopled, the houses strung out between us and the mountain; the school bus had few stops on the last couple of miles of the road. We bought Michele a Connemara pony for the challenge and for love. I fetched him bales of hay on the bicycle trailer after our car sat down, and would linger at the stable door at dusk, breathing his warm air, nose to nose.

Our years with livestock were some of the richest of all. Ethna had initially drawn the line at goats, but ended up making cheese, along with home-baked bread and many gallons of fruit and flower wine. I did the milking, often by torchlight in the shed beside the stream that ran through a corner of the acre, communing with a matronly white Saanen as I coaxed the jet into the bucket. That special squeeze had to be learned. So did the fact that goats (like the geese, and I loved them, too) needed too much grazing space on a single, crowded acre. A dairy must also have kids, whose little horns, the book said, could be disbudded with a heated screwdriver – a day we ended up tipsy on our elderflower wine.

The "simple" life is far from that, even with expert books to advise on everything, and it is sometimes fraught with clumsy, abhorrent violence. Ducklings for eating have their necks wrung at ten weeks (those silky white wings trembling under my arm – just the once!), hens have theirs wrung when they get sick or old, and a Christmas goose might need a hatchet. The big, flapping thornback rays, caught on the spillet, were killed and butchered on the strand. I won't go on: the supermarket spares us such petty murders.

The demanding daily rounds of activity, played out in the appalling weather of the 1980s, sealed us off from national hardship in the world beyond the hill – that, after all, was part of the philosophy. But too many cold, drenching summers and Ethna's sudden, unexpected allergy to bee stings brought an eventual end to the hives. The goats and geese had gone, and as rural predators – fox, dog, otter, stoat, hedgehog – repeatedly culled our ducks and hens, the will to restock them diminished. Michele went off to college, so Báinín disappeared to thrill another ten-year-old in Connemara.

The acre was still growing ample food within its maze of windbreak fences and fuchsia hedges, but was now very quiet. I was free to join David Cabot, our ornithologist friend across the lake, in two expeditions to east Greenland, while Ethna took over the garden and the story of Another Life.

The expeditions were to study and film barnacle geese. A few thousand of them winter on the Connacht islands but breed on the Greenland cliffs. The High Arctic wilderness leaves nature in sole possession of the raw and virgin landscape, so that everything that moved – musk oxen, snowy hares, a wandering wolf, polar bears on the fjord – was in command of a life quite indifferent to the human species. I returned to Mayo, its lush and jumbled vegetation, its teeming if commonplace range of species, with an extra feeling for our need to know more about them.

Curiosity, always my driving force, partners an aesthetic sense alive to form and colour: the wide theatre of sky and sea, the detail of plants and wildlife. The poet Michael Longley, long our friend and summer neighbour in this landscape, has described how, at first, the hugeness of its space and horizons draws the eye, then the intricate middle distance of little fields and drystone walls. "Finally, you end up on your hands and knees, almost at prayer, looking at the faces of flowers."

It is this kind of awe that I have tried to temper with scientific fact, scouring the indexes of thousands of books on our walls and exploring current research through wireless broadband beaming in from the islands to our gable. For years of Another Life (years of carbon paper, Tippex and scrunched-up sheets of paper) my copy and drawing were sent by post – three miles each way on the bike, often in strong headwinds and horizontal rain. Now ours is an electronic cottage, of downloads, image files and emails.

The wider world has changed, too, as ecology has seized the attention of Earth's most destructive species. Relations with the rest of life, its ecosystems and biodiversity, have taken on quite a new reality and respect. A steady flow of popular books on Ireland's wild flowers, animals, birds and sea life has matched the rise of national expertise and a growing role for the natural world in the school experience of the young. Mine has been the marginal contribution of an inquisitive and fond interpreter, not a "naturalist". That title is more properly reserved for those whose lifetime passions for observing and researching add to the scientific knowledge of nature, often with no material reward.

Meanwhile, what has happened to our local landscape? Gone are fields of oats and the ridges of potatoes beside every house. Gone are silage meitheals with their big farmhouse dinners, and the spring exodus of families to cut turf on the mountain. Gone are donkeys with "slippers" of untrimmed hooves lest they sink, and cattle grazing the "long acre" of the roadsides. Stony roads have been tarred, and the wonderful, babbling ford where the boreen crossed the mountain river (dipper, wagtails, sand martins) is culverted to link with the new car park behind the strand. More holiday homes line the brow of the hill, but the boom years expired in good time to save the view, and the men who did the building are back in good homes of their own. As the promise of farming revives, for every pasture drifting into rushes another is cleared and resown.

For many of the early years, Another Life in The Irish Times provided virtually our sole income – this from a classically chance encounter on Grafton Street in Dublin on the eve of our departure to the west. "You won't be back in six months?" asked Douglas Gageby, the paper's editor, quizzically – then made his generous invitation to me to write a column. We had other portable skills besides, gained in television experience. As our livestock later dwindled and with our daughter launched on her own career in the film industry, Ethna and I began making documentaries for RTÉ and TnaG. They paid for a new roof, double glazing, a new car and rare foreign holidays with friends. But really, living in our landscape, who would want to be anywhere else?

After thirty-eight years of Another Life, as I think Ethna and Michele would agree, most of it turned out fine.

On the acre, the trees we planted so randomly whenever a seedling came to hand have grown to an awesome maturity, each bracing the other in ocean storms. They have enveloped the old plywood hen-house and its rampant fuchsia hedges, and now crowd in upon the glade where my big polytunnel shudders in the gusts, but holds. It is my all-weather palace, with earphones for music and a comfortable director's chair.

Filling it with many kinds of vegetables is pretty much all I can manage now.

This is the close of a great adventure in living, with the partner of fifty years who has helped make so much of it happen. Decades of often strenuous activity in pure ocean air, and a diet of fresh vegetables and fish, would, you might think, have guaranteed an exceptionally fit old age. They have certainly helped me survive some drastic repercussions from the heavy smoking of my city newspaper years. (You want to see my scars?) I am now eighty-two, and their legacy limits my energy, but still, irreducibly, I enjoy helping things to grow, walking in the wind and listening to the birds, and writing about nature as long as The Irish Times has room.

Michael Viney
Thallabawn, Co Mayo

Early years

November 12th 1977

Spectacular weather in the first winter

When the roots of an upturned dock are meticulously washed, they are the yellow of Benares brass. I might not have known this but for the weather we have had these past six weeks: wave after wave of rain borne in on gales that began with the equinox and forgot to stop.

The dug-over soil of the field has been hammered smooth and the stream growls and rumbles at night, digesting the boulders brought down from the hill. From the top of the mountain to the edge of the sea the pores of the land are full, so that each new downpour must run off as it falls, flooding the fields behind the strand. The sheep make way for swans on the cold, new water.

So we have lost the autumn and are well into the kind of winter that is supposed to wear us down and make us wish we had never left Dublin. But one advantage of living in an "exposed place", as the Met Office has it, is that the weather has a saving sense of theatre.

When Hilaire Belloc dismissed the midlands as sodden and unkind, he was speaking of England. But he might just as well have been thinking of

9

Mullingar on a wet Sunday, or some other place where the sky is trapped in a circle of dripping rocks' nests.

Here at the western edge, we look out into an immense amphitheatre where the weather can perform in its entirety and do several things at once at different planes and corners of the stage. Clouds pile up into chorus lines, black squalls leap in from the wings, curtains are drawn across by hailstorms or lift from the horizon in magical clearance (Fabergé skies of gold and blue enamel). Highs and lows, fronts and troughs – we see them coming and going, and know the shapes they make in the sky.

So, whatever they may be stuck with on the other side of the mountain, we are exposed not only to gale gusts but to all the other dramatic humours of the atmosphere: the weather is a non-stop spectacular.

We follow the radio forecasts, if only to hear the Met Office warning the rest of the country of the weather we already have. As in so much else, Dublin seems to see itself at the heart of the Irish climate, imposing its bright spells and scattered showers on the country at large, and sounding quite shocked when a storm insists on barging right across to the capital. But if it sometimes seems to us as if the forecasts are tailored more to the city commuter than to the countryman or fisherman, there is always the chance that some sun may be tucked away for us in the Icelandic isobars left unread. In practice, we trust our own barometer.

This is supposed to be the time – at least in urban prejudice – when the small western farmer climbs into his long johns and prepares to hibernate. The long johns, certainly – I have them on myself – but my neighbours are also abroad in oilskins, working with their dogs. This is the time for breeding, for running the rams with the mountain ewes. One curly-horned stud on his way up the hill made a sudden and prodigious leap into my field, clearing a man's height of ditch and fence. He was quickly rounded up, but his leap reminded me of one job that must be done this month: the laying of the hawthorn hedge.

This is a job that should be done every few years, but our thorn bushes are scrawny old wrecks, cowering away from the westerly winds and leaning far in from the top of the ditch. When the tractor ploughed for me a year ago, the driver wisely kept his distance from the thorn, so a long strip of good land still waits for cultivation. In laying a hedge, the taller stems are cut half through and then bent down to intertwine with others. The laid stems keep enough sap to send up new growth to thicken the hedge and make it stock-proof. I would like to interplant the thorn with fuchsia and honeysuckle, but that is a long way down the list of priorities.

Before the frosts come, I must bury the pipe that brings the water from the hill. Then I shall have a system which I know through every inch from source to tap (as I need to – the nearest plumber is twenty miles away).

Hedge and pipe are two fairly strenuous undertakings which now queue up for attention. How well does a middle-aged city desk worker, who never played squash with the Beautiful People, adapt to this kind of hard labour? Scarcely a day of the past three months has passed without some kind of physical work, much of it quite taxing. Every morning during that time I have woken stiff and sore, often groaning out loud from some new punishment to back and shoulders, arms and hands. From the start I have tried to save my back – one slipped disc and we're in trouble.

But it is not always easy to judge if a rock is too heavy to lift alone, or if the time has come to take a break. The scale of effort is so much greater than I have known before.

Carpentry is no longer a delicate affair of batten and blockboard and dinky screws, but rather of six-inch nails and relentless rip-cuts down two-inch planks. And fieldwork here is not gardening, filling the intervals between cups of coffee, but long use of a dry day while we have it.

If it hurts so much, why do I do it? Why not sit in the window and write and earn money to pay to have things done? Obviously, I do it because I enjoy using my muscles outdoors in work that helps me and my family. It may not stand up to economic scrutiny: I am certainly not optimising the market value of my time. But it makes me feel good, the transient aches and pains notwithstanding. Like the kick I get from standing on my own acre, it is probably sheer atavism and none the worse for that.

Meanwhile, a friendly reader in Ballina thinks we should buy geese to eat some of our redundant potatoes. He suggests we get ten of them to fatten for Christmas and the freezer. He also reminds us of a portable henhouse which would move six hens to a new patch of grass every few days, and so help provide eggs economically. We'll find out about it. But if the geese need penning, to keep them away from the spring cabbage, will that mean more wire netting? The last roll we bought, of the coarsest mesh, cost £13.25 in Westport for a paltry fifty yards. Geese by all means, but not to lay golden eggs.

December 4th 1978

Equality studies

Waking in the dark the other morning to the drumming of rain and the rattle of the stream in flood, I began to wonder aloud if one of us should go out and take a spade to clear the gully that saves the shed from flooding. It would be too bad if the water reached our hard-won bags of cement. Whether I actually sent Ethna out, or whether she volunteered and I assented, will remain a matter of family debate. At any rate, she went, looking fetchingly gamine in my oilskins and sou'wester, while I lay on in bed, meditating on our new interpretations of equality.

The self-supporting country life is a test for any marriage, let alone one in which the wife has been used to having her own career, an executive salary and as much independence as a mother can expect. For a start, husband and wife have to live together, not merely joining each other for breakfast, evening television and what's left of the weekend after golf, the supermarket and Sunday lunchtime drinks.

It has not been too much of a shock for us, because even in Dublin we preferred each other's company. But for some couples, the sudden onset of proximity could be quite dismaying. The husband can't be got out from under the feet; the wife must be listened to and comprehended.

Whole days are spent together. The more equal the partnership, the less risk of secret doubts to feed on discomfort or crisis. No intelligent or even half-emancipated wife is going to let herself be hijacked into such a change of lifestyle. But what can be hard to judge in advance is the volume of chores that go with it.

A wife may positively look forward to battling the elements shoulder to shoulder with her man – but not reckon with burrowing into the turf stack for the hundredth time in search of one dry sod.

The self-supporting diet, which spurns processed foods, takes extra time to prepare. In Dublin, our dinner went into a self-timing oven at breakfast time and was already cooking when Ethna came home from the office. It used a lot of expensive meat. Now, we use very little, but often eat three or four vegetables at a meal, which have to be harvested and cleaned and cooked in different ways. In place of the oven casserole is a stack of saucepans with sooty bottoms.

One of these days, we will have filled the cubic inches of the freezer and will have to start taking food out of it. Meanwhile, we harvest and hoard. Until I began to help, I just had no idea what a back-breaking job it is merely to trim off the sprouts.

My appetite has grown prodigiously, so that Ethna must bake four whole-meal loaves at a time – using the freezer to keep the bread fresh. I eat a lot of potatoes too.

And the geese, ducks and chickens eat two buckets of potatoes a day, which Ethna has dug, washed, sorted, boiled and mashed.

All this has been made even more time-consuming in a kitchen which has been gutted and slowly rebuilt around her, and which only now, in stormy weather, I am fitting with proper shelves and worktops.

When she looks at the lifestyles of her neighbours, Ethna is given little to complain of. Suppose she had ten children rather than one. How often would she leave the kitchen then, except to feed the fowl or hang the washing out? But it was never our intention to follow the traditional work roles of the country. Ethna's picture of rural self-reliance was never framed by the kitchen window. She enjoys outdoor manual work as much as I do, and is fit for all but the heaviest of it.

So now it is a priority to streamline the housework through some time-and-motion study, some sensible solutions (such as thatching the turf stack to keep it dry) and by sharing it out more equitably. I can start, it is suggested, by tidying things away after me and by accepting that washing-up also includes wiping the worktops and sweeping the floor. Our daughter Michele, for her part, must stop dreaming over The Waltons and turn to help the Vineys.

Whether or not she was deprived of mother love through spending a couple of hours in the afternoon in the care of a childminder, she did miss being taught to share in the housework. When a working mother comes home at night, it is faster and easier for her to whip through the chores herself rather than take time to involve her offspring. We have to remember this when Michele finds it hard to buckle down to our new work routines, and not expect an immediate transformation into a diligent, disciplined country child. (Immediately, of course, she makes me eat my words by creeping off, unbidden, to set the breakfast table at bedtime.)

Ethna and I find it easier to plan together than to work together, if this means physically sharing a task. In our professional careers, we have been used to working alone and to rapid problem-solving. We are also fairly stubborn. So we are known to bicker – but with more sound than fury, now that we know why we do it.

This week, for example, after days of storm and rain, the chickens were paddling on an over-grazed swamp. We decided to uproot their run – a structure like a freeform tennis court – and plant the seven-foot fence again around a fresh plot of grass.

It had to be done quickly, in a lull between gales, and we finished it in the opening rain squalls of a new southwesterly. It was a job involving crowbar and mallet. It meant holding things at awkward angles and keeping one's head out of the way. It meant agreeing on distances and on fine points of geometry.

I don't think I'd like to hear a tape of us – The Tailor and Ansty wouldn't be in it.

But even at the tops of our voices, we were really enjoying ourselves.

September 1st 1979
Predator, prisoner, nearly a pet

The sound beyond the drystone wall was sudden and strange: a stampede of horses, an avalanche of rocks – something almost as thunderous as that. In the next second, a great flock of starlings swept over the wall in a torrent of flickering wings, whirring so close to my head that I threw up my arms involuntarily. It was the third or fourth time in a week that these birds had given me a fright with their manoeuvres, exploding into flight from a meadow beside me or scything across the landscape in mass formation like a thousand little hedge-hopping fighter planes. But they were beautiful to watch, weaving and swirling within the flock to the patterns of a dark kaleidoscope.

We welcome the migration of the starlings as a signal of autumn and renewal of our contact with wild things. All summer, as the cars of the visitors besieged our quiet roads and tractors invaded the fields to mow them bare, wildlife lies low in the hedges and ditches, and we are working too hard and moving about too busily to notice much of what is happening in the natural underworld. But sometimes, as happened the other night, its events are forced on our attention.

Our venturesome ducks, led by Fred the drake, have recently grown tired of the daily bullying from Claudius, the gander, and his heavy mob of geese, and found a way out of the hollow to more peaceful pastures.

They climb around the waterfall where the stream splashes into our land, paddle through the shallows in the dark beneath the bridge, push around the sheet of iron that keeps out the sheep, and emerge in a rocky meadow on the other side of the road.

We can see them in the distance, foraging in convoy, suddenly very small and vulnerable on the windy expanse of the hill.

When the chicks first came home at dusk one short, we immediately supposed the worst and went looking for a scatter of feathers. But a quacking at the gable next morning was the missing bird demanding breakfast.

She went missing two more nights until, rushing out to feeding time from a thicket in the hollow, she gave herself away. Deep in a clump of brambles and meadowsweet was a nest with seven eggs.

After our abortive attempts this spring to get the ducks to hatch their eggs in the safety of the fowl house (they let the eggs get cold, or ate them), we were delighted to think that the birds might confound us by doing things the "natural" way. In a month's time, perhaps, the mother would emerge with seven yellow ducklings behind her.

But we knew all the odds were against it. If ducks are rotten mothers in confined conditions, their attempts at hatching outside in the undergrowth are at the mercy of every passing rat, fox or stoat.

In calm weather, the loudest sound in our night is the rumble of the surf along the shore. So an anguished quacking in the hollow at midnight brought us to the window at once. The white shape in the blackness was our nesting duck, running up and down outside the fowl house, beseeching to be let in. We hurried out with a flash lamp to see what had scared her from her eggs.

The hedgehog was a predator we hadn't considered. We did meet one a couple of autumns ago, ambling down the boreen on a sunny evening, but that had seemed a charming curiosity. Most of our landscape is so open and severe that we don't think to look for the fauna of the bosky hedge bottoms. In our garden in suburban Dublin, a bristly shape squashed flat on the drive was the first we knew of our resident hedgehog. And now here among the brambles, hunched up in the glare of the flash lamp, was the spiky bandit munching on an egg.

Hedgehogs are insectivores, with an unsurpassed appetite for slugs that makes them very popular with gardeners. But they will also eat eggs when they can, and even small birds, which is why, in pheasant country, they have so often ended up on the gamekeeper's gibbet. We were not disposed to kill our hedgehog, but we did plan to move him on.

The nest was so deep in the brambles, he was going to be difficult to reach. And whether his prickles were sharp or not, they would certainly abound in fleas. (The spines prevent the hedgehog from grooming.) It was Ethna's inspiration to extract him with our big turf tongs and imprison him in a tea chest. Then, since the six remaining eggs were still warm, we tried to persuade the duck to go back to them, but the trauma of being pushed off her nest in the dark by an implacable, heavy-breathing intruder had scared her too thoroughly, so that is another six ducks that will never reach our freezer.

Next morning, we tipped the hedgehog into a nursery coop (a wire-netting cage, for keeping chicks in) and had a good look at him. He uncurled obligingly and roamed around the coop, looking for a way out.

He then stood on his hind legs and rested dainty paws on the netting, so that we could inspect him nose to nose.

He was a much more substantial and personable mammal than we had expected.

It seemed a pity about his fleas. British hedgehogs are reported to have about 100 fleas each, but their Irish cousins seem to make do with fourteen or fewer.

Recording this in An Irish Beast Book (Blackstaff Press, 1975), Dr James S Fairley warns that "hedgehog fleas will attack man savagely when hungry. Despite its undoubted attractiveness, the prudent will, therefore, hesitate before bringing a hedgehog indoors." In response to an observation on the hedgehog flea, Archaeopsylla erinacei, the British scientific journal The Entomologist's Gazette once unbent sufficiently to print the following letter: "Dear sir, The fleas of an Edgehorgc is the same as ours I know because once I was looking at an Edgehorgc and a flea jumped off it onto my nose and then into my Highbrows. I waited to see what would happen and it lived there several days though what it lived on I don't Know it only bit me once. You could see it quite plain, I used to look at it in the Mirror and Mrs F. saw it too, but one day it was gone we don't know where. Perhaps it saw another Edgehorgc."

We looked closely – but not too closely – at our prisoner, and it seemed to be very clean indeed. But any temptation to make a pet of him was settled when he found a weak spot in the coop and disappeared over the ditch.

December 6ᵗʰ 1980
A two-fisted milker

For many years of my working life, half-past five in the evening was the time to put on my coat, pick up my briefcase and head off to catch the bus home. When I picture this now, I can see the oily glitter of wet pavements in Westmoreland Street after I left the Irish Times office in Dublin and feel the icy shock of the wind that waited beyond the lee of the Ballast Office. But the Ballast Office is demolished and my evening routine has changed. Half-past five is now the time when I go to milk the goat.

It made sense to share the daily milking, if Barby could be persuaded to accept two different sets of hands at her udder. The evening milking clashed with cooking dinner. And if Ethna alone had the knack in her fingers and the necessary rapport with the goat, what would happen if she got flu or had to travel to a funeral or even (to admit the unthinkable) insisted on breakfast in bed? So it is she who wraps up warmly at half-past seven each morning and picks her way cautiously across the frosty footbridge, while I take her place – still most inexpertly – at the other end of the day.

For a start, there are so many things to carry: two separate buckets of feed, one of lukewarm drinking water, the empty pail for the milk, the tub of udder cream, the flannel wrung out in hot water and disinfectant (with which to wipe the udder without paralysing the goat) and the 12-volt flash lamp. All these can, in fact, be carried on one journey, if someone else opens the door.

Dusk falls slowly here on the open Atlantic coast. Long after the sun has dropped into an inky rim of cloud at the horizon, the afterglow lingers above the islands. I step out to a cyclorama of deep, smoky blue. But down in the hollow it is already dark and the goats begin to bleat impatiently as they see the flash lamp approaching.

There is quite a mixed community lodging in the shed these nights.

Barby and Alice, her kid, take up most of it, sleeping on an ever-deepening mattress of rushes and spoilt hay. The ducks still roost at one end, pending construction of new quarters, and they have now been joined by the Christmas goose, who was finding her tea chest lonely and persisted in tagging along when the ducks went to bed.

And finally there is Sooty, the cat, who has taken up residence in the warmest corner, under Barby's haybox.

Since she was banished from the kitchen to keep her away from the dairying, we can only salute her effrontery in finding a bed within inches of Barby's udder. In folklore, it was the hare that suckled the cow by night; we have heard nothing so kinky about cats and goats.

Once Barby's nose has reached the dairy nuts, a certain urgency creeps into my movements. When she was delivered to us from the Wicklow Hills this autumn, her owner expressed the hope that we were fast, two-fisted milkers, "because Barby stands still only while she's eating". Indeed, as she chases the last nut around the bottom of the bucket, her rear, offside leg begins to twitch. A few seconds later, if the milk pail has not been snatched up, one dainty but shitty hoof has been plunged into it.

The milking is, therefore, a race against time – particularly since Ethna caught me upping the ration of nuts to buy myself a few extra minutes of stillness. But nothing of my inner turmoil must be communicated to Barby: panic and curses will make her nervous (and set the ducks gabbling hysterically in the shadows). No – she must be petted and crooned to and her udder (or elder, as I am learning to call it) wiped down as if there were all the time in the world; only then will her teats be full and flowing.

There were nights at the beginning when I was sure I would never learn to milk with both hands at once. The goat's teat requires a special, two-part squeeze, which can seem as difficult as the fingering of the uilleann pipes, and again and again the milk has gone spurting up my sleeve. But there are more nights now when the knack and the rhythm coincide and a great calm descends within the shed as the two jets of milk converge, foaming in the pail.

As I crouch there on the rushes in a golden cave of light, I listen to the sounds around me – the hiss of the milk, the rumbling in one of Barby's stomachs, the sotto voce debate among the ducks, the tattle of the stream outside, and perhaps the night wind moaning – and I sometimes (but not too often) think of the number 25 bus still inching up the Liffey quays, its windows fogged and weeping with the breath of a thousand sighs.

Autumn is the usual time for mating goats, and we do need to get young Alice in kid so that she will be milking when her mother goes dry. But we feel she is still a little small, and intend to wait until February before taking her fifty miles across the mountains to the nearest pedigree Saanen billy. Meanwhile, we have to hope that no whiff of our goats' presence will drift on the wind to the enormous, shaggy puck who is lodging with a farmer a mile up the hill.

We have no idea of his breed.

"He's a Charolais!" jokes the farmer, pointing to the ochreous colour of his prodigiously tangled coat. But while somebody went to the trouble of having him dehorned, he last changed hands for £40, bought by a farmer in the hills near Westport who was told that a good, strong puck would graze down the briars on his land.

His sojourn here is to service the only other goats in the locality besides our own. One was wished on the farmer by friends in Tipperary, who found her coming down the stairs from the children's bedroom and decided enough was enough. Another was found as a kid beside the road along Killary Harbour and is presumed to be an orphan of the feral goats of the mountains. Each is only half the size of Barby, but they have made enough of a harem for the puck to set him dancing on his hind legs for days.

We had never been close to a billy goat before and so had never smelled the distinctive scent that has got all goats a bad name. At the time of his rutting, it had penetrated even the farmer's house. It is actually the product of the billy's musk glands, behind the horns, and he spreads it around by rubbing his head on his females.

We did not smell it at its worst but, like the farmer, couldn't quite think what it reminded us of: a sweet, acrid odour that might have been silage, gunpowder, the lees of wine, and yet was not any of these.

To Ethna, the smell recalled a year in her youth when she worked in New York, mixing perfumes. One of her precious ingredients, which gave the scent body and made it last on the skin, was extracted from the musk glands of the civet cat.

April 14th 1984

Turtles on tour

Just over the hill where the road swings north there is a lofty view across the sea – to Clare Island and, in clear weather, to the Bills Rocks, almost twenty miles away on the horizon. On days of heavy swell I sometimes stop my bicycle there, one foot on the ditch, to watch the great collisions of wave and rock.

The slow, shining explosions that engulf the distant Bills are all the more dramatic for knowing at first hand those isolated crags and arches and being able to imagine the mighty concussions, the white towers leaping up to dash the sea pinks from the highest ledges. The intervening miles of ocean are deceptively innocent of waves, but as the swell nears the shore, it grounds upon a hidden reef and heaps up over it, and spills into a sudden, tumbling chevron of foam. In these two eruptions, near and far, the whole inner commotion of the sea is betrayed.

It is not possible to live beside the Atlantic and not want to know what goes on inside it. Or, rather, it would not be possible if our schooling were not dreamed up by men in city offices. I grew up beside the English Channel and was given dogfish to dissect in school – but these lessons in anatomy, as I recall, had little to do with the living sea. Here in Mayo, I was pleased to hear from my daughter that a biology class was actually taken to the shore, but how many of them, I wonder, will end up knowing a diatom from a mollusc or understanding that the sea, too, has its seasons? I sometimes try to imagine the hidden landscape of our corner of the Atlantic: its sandy slopes and plains, its rocky bluffs and gullies, its groves of waving kelp. The old admiralty chart we keep on the wall shows the soundings of 1S4H, and from the scattered fathoms I can trace the contours of the seabed as it rises to the glacial sill of Killary. These I can furnish with images borrowed from Jacques Cousteau's underwater films or from my own braver years with mask and snorkel. But they are not the chill, sombre wonders known to the scuba divers who come to Clare Island or dare the crystal canyons of the Bills.

My thoughts about the sea and my knowledge of it were nourished in a very seminal way by the books of an exceptional woman whose name most people know for something else entirely. Rachel Carson wrote Silent Spring and thus earned fame and gratitude for her warnings about persistent pesticides. But this might never have reached the audience it did were it not for the impact of her earlier books: The Sea Around Us, Under the Sea Wind and The Edge of the Sea. I am lucky to have all three in one volume, called simply The Sea, published by MacGibbon & Kee twenty years ago.

Rachel Carson was actually a marine biologist, a civil servant with the U.S. Fish & Wildlife Service until she resigned to write. She was a vivid, poetic communicator, a disciplined scientist and an uncommonly sensitive ecologist. In my favourite glimpse of her she is clambering over a rocky shore in Maine, at dead of night, to return a large starfish she had taken from the morning tide: "The starfish was at home at the lowest level of these tides of the August moon and to that level it must be returned. I took a flashlight and made my way down over the slippery rockweeds. It was an eerie world; ledges curtained with weed and boulders that by day were familiar landmarks seemed to loom larger than I remembered and to have assumed unfamiliar shapes, every projecting mass thrown into bold relief by the shadows. Everywhere I looked, directly in the beam of my flashlight or obliquely in the half-illuminated gloom, crabs were scuttling about. Boldly and possessively they inhabited the weed-shrouded rocks. All the grotesqueness of their form accentuated, they seemed to have transformed this once familiar place into a goblin world."

It is thanks to Rachel Carson that I can sense the awakenings of springtime not only in the fields that run down to the shore, but in the sea itself. She has made me aware of the seasonal overturn by which the winter-chilled water at the surface slides heavily down and the warmer, deeper water rises to replace it, carrying up minerals to nourish the microscopic plants and thus, as one consumes another, the teeming animals of the sea. Such a simple insight has helped me belong more completely to the planet.

My own discoveries, occasionally exotic, among the dead things the sea has deposited near our door – whales, dolphins, turtles – has brought me into correspondence with an amateur naturalist called Gabriel King who seems set on a one-man crusade of marine conservation. The creatures of his concern are among the more mysterious of Ireland's marine fauna: the turtles that reach these waters from warmer latitudes and which, at least until very recently, were seen as mere drifting waifs and strays, doomed to die of cold.

I have found two such turtles, both dead, on the shore. One, a little

Kemp's ridley from the Gulf of Mexico, is now pickled in the Natural History Museum in Dublin. The other, a large loggerhead, also probably from the West Indies, is remembered by its carapace on my studio wall. But Mr King's crusade is chiefly for a turtle I have not seen – though quite a few Irish fishermen now have – called the leatherback, or Dermochelys coriacea.

This is easily the largest turtle in the world – five feet long is an average size – but instead of a shell of horny plates, it has a carapace like hard black rubber ridges from front to back. It is an extremely powerful swimmer, feeds almost entirely on jellyfish and has the useful capacity of maintaining an inner body temperature in cold water almost 18 Celsius warmer than its surroundings.

As recently as 1961, the leatherback was treated like a rarity – especially when it turned up in northern European waters – and was thought to number no more than 1,000 in the world. Now that its nesting beaches have been plotted more thoroughly, it appears there could be 40,000 adult females alone. And the leatherback is now recognised – by such experts as Dr LD Brongersma of the Netherlands – as a regular summer visitor to France at least, munching jellyfish as it swims, and turning back south, possibly to west Africa, before wintry cold sets in in northern waters.

Gabriel King became involved with Ireland's leatherbacks last summer when one was taken alive in a driftnet off Quilty, Co Clare. He persuaded the fishermen to let it go and discovered in the process that no one seemed to have considered if a turtle was a protected fauna species under the Irish Wildlife Act, 1976. He has since received the Minister's assurance that it is.

In making his case for the leatherback as a regular summer guest in our waters, he has also amassed thirty-two recordings of the turtle over the past ten years, mostly along the west coast. The majority of the twenty-five specimens collected were taken alive.

The leatherback is prone to entanglement in driftnets and lobster pots, and its skin, for all its apparent toughness, is quite tender.

But it doesn't need "putting out of its misery": the apparent tears in its eyes are from eating all those jellyfish.

Mr King likes to put it this way: "Credit should be given to the Irish fishermen – especially in Co Kerry – for having released their remarkable 'catches' without subjecting them to the unnecessary trauma and distress of being towed into port for display."

June 14ᵗʰ 1986
An average, boring old day

"You write about the odd things," a reader says, "but try giving us an average, boring old day – then I might know if I'd like it." Yesterday will do.

4.45am: We beat the alarm – must be in training. Ethna sits up in bed to write, lost at once in her story. I pad out to the studio to catch up on letters. A still, pewtery morning, islands stretched out in a haze, the surf silent. Write to Norway, to a hut above the fjord, where a young German is translating Another Life for a book the Greens might like. What, he needs to know, is a JCB? What are sea rods? Some of the headings come out well in German: for "Wimp of the West" read "Softe des Westens".

7.15am: Short jog before breakfast – just as far as Paddy's silage pit. Jeered by grey crow on an ESB pole.

Try the new batch of rye bread at breakfast. Well risen but still a bit soggy.

Ethna quite put out. Radio tells about the plan to put mailboxes at the ends of boreens, to save the postman time. Michael Fergus, just retired, used to wade the channel to the last house.

8.15am: Feed hens, collect two eggs; feed ducks, steal one egg. "Steal" because it feels like that: the duck has a drake, covers her egg, has obvious hopes. I sidle by as they shovel up their mash, the egg palmed. Measure the rain in the gauge on the lawn; 0.5 millimetres. Better than May, 167 millimetres, over twice the normal level.

8.30am: We are a two-wheelbarrow family. Ethna takes the small one to Báinín's field, to shake nitrogen on the bare bits. What isn't bare he has dunged on, and thus won't eat. We tether him at the gable to eat the lawn until rain has melted the nitrogen: he'll have to spend his nights in the hen run.

With the big barrow, I start shifting the last ton of cow muck we tipped outside Michele's window. She is in Paris, au pairing to improve her French. How we gonna keep her down on the farm, after she's seen Paree? We're not – or not if she can help it.

Meg runs at my heels as I trundle down and up the path. (Thank goodness for the slope: the heavy, wet manure almost runs away with the barrow.) The cats laze among the strawberry flowers, watching. Bimbo and her kitten got into the cold frame last night and squashed the sweetcorn seedlings; they see all the plastic cloches as summer pavilions put up specially for them. Cinnamon gives me less trouble, but he does piss on the turf.

Bumblebees. Take off my anorak – about time! It's June, but where are the flies? Three bumblebees burrow into the catmint, grateful for a decent drop of nectar.

10.30am: The postman's van at the gate. Among the mail, a Dublin housewife with two daughters wants to say how much she enjoys WWOOFing – working weekends on organic farms.

WWOOFers would shift this muck for me, but we're not the hospitable, outgoing kind: I should have a beard and play the tin whistle.

11am: A young neighbour arrives with an American cousin: could they take Báinín to ride? Keep him for a week, we say. (But no one has that much spare grass.)

Noon: A farmer and his collie gather sheep in the rocky field across the road.

I lean on my fork to watch, taking pleasure in the work of an intelligent dog. But the sheep are uncooperative and keep breaking as they near the gate.

Another neighbour, passing in his car, pulls up and gets out to help in the last push. I feel mortified, as usual – I was just standing there. Nine years living alongside farmers and I still never know when to offer a hand.

1pm: Egg salad for lunch. I could eat fresh-laid eggs at every meal – before cholesterol, did people worry? The hens have another two when I take them their feed. Rooks and jackdaws perch on the fence, waiting their turn at the bowl.

3pm: Finish the muck at last and turn to planting out winter cabbage. On my knees, scooping holes, when a strange sound rasps out from the field banks beside me: not quite a belch, not quite a growl, but a beastly, mammalian sort of a sound. I creep close and peer into the dark behind the nettles. It comes again at intervals, but its source eludes me. Settle for a hedgehog – perhaps a family? Creep away again, delighted.

3.30pm: New machine. Ethna has been trying to mow the steep bank of the hollow, across the stream where the pony won't go. She is using our new Italian machine, but the growth in this sheltery place keeps choking it into silence. I am appealed to: "I've been waiting years to mow that grass!" I take down the scythe and open up an arc into the soft, green stuff. Finding my rhythm, I begin to enjoy it…swish…swish. The sun comes out and sweat begins to drip from my eyebrows – which, I suppose, is what they're for.

4.30pm: Fish van at the gate: spotless, well-iced, worth a medal from BIM. Our own ray in the freezer is almost gone. We can't start fishing with the spillet until we're on top of the planting. We buy plaice and cod and fresh mackerel. Do we eat the mackerel or freeze them for bait? Prudence wins.

5pm: Too sunny now for planting (the seedlings wilt). Start hoeing weeds off a bed, to plant out French beans under plastic, but decide the hedge needs cutting back first. Get out electric hedge cutter – not the luxury it seems when you have six-foot hedges within hedges, like Hampton Court maze. Plug in 200 feet of cable, bring end of cable over right shoulder, where it won't get cut, and prepare to concentrate. Goes through fuchsia like butter – "Magic!" as Selwyn Froggitt would say. Get carried away and do the next hedge as well.

6pm: Dinner. "How is it," asks Ethna, "that however many potatoes I do, there are never enough left over for potato salad?"

7pm: Night chores. Bring in sack of turf to fill the box and bucket of clods to bank down the range. Take Báinín down to the hen run. Close in hens. Lure ducks into shed with bowl of mash. Passing belt of infant Sitkas (for more shelter), start pulling grass from around them. Stop after a dozen: the back's at me.

8pm: Nothing on RTÉ – is there ever? Take Meg for walk around the boreen. Thorn hedges withered by the Big Wind, willows barely in leaf, ferns just uncoiled above the primroses. Fields green, but cattle come running to me, mistaking my figure. The hay lorry swoops down the hill, blowing its horn like a French camion.

"I don't see any dead beasts," I said to a neighbour a week or two back. He looked at me quizzically. " 'Not a drum was heard, not a funeral note' – do you know that one? 'We buried him darkly at dead of night, The sods with our bayonets turning.'"

9pm: To bed, with the London Review of Books.

August 23rd 1986
Fishing while sleeping

The turn of the tide is one of Earth's more mysterious moments, and on no two beaches on any one day is its time exactly the same. The cosmic pull of the moon, the oscillation of seas in their basins, the shape and contour of particular shores all go to make the first landward lurch of water a peculiarly local event. Even with a tide table, adjusted for summertime and the distance from Inishbofin to Thallabawn, we sometimes get it wrong.

Hence our breathless presence at the sea's edge the other morning at half an hour on the dark side of sunrise, peering out across blurred and shadowy surf for a glimpse of the orange buoys at each end of the nightline. Rain delivered by a brisk south wind hissed steadily upon the sand.

If the spillet was not recovered now, at the very bottom of the tide, it would have to stay there for another twelve hours. Its catch of fish would break free or be minced by crabs; a storm could come out of nowhere.

Stoically shedding a carapace of clothes, I advanced into the breakers to seize a buoy and haul the anchor. Prodigious weight on the line and the first swirl of a ray's wing at the surface helped us put rain and wind and indigo horizon resolutely out of mind.

The heaviest catch was on the hooks strung out across the mouth of the channel where a swift, brown flood from the mountain was churning the surf and staining the sea far beyond. We have always believed that this miniature estuary, delivering earthworms and nyws and beetle grubs into the waves, must whet the appetites not only of flounders and dabs, but of the more predatory scavengers – thornback rays and dogfish – that come to seek out the long line of mackerel baits.

Like all the shark family, their senses are acute. The ray even shares with its bigger hunting cousins the highly developed sensory pores that can detect the electrical activity in living things. By this means alone a shark can find a flatfish concealed in the sand. (It can also, for that matter, hear the sound a muscle makes when it flexes: stick your thumbs in your ears and curl your fingers and that gives you some idea.)

None of this, of course, is much help in finding a small chunk of dead mackerel in a darkened sea, beneath breakers that are churning up the sand, in an estuary already fogged with particles of peat from the mountain. A turbot, for example, would not attempt it. But the rays have the shark's capacity for scent, which has doomed them to be caught on baited long lines as plentifully by night as by day.

People who know the thornback only as wings of rosy flesh on the fishmonger's slab can have no idea of the powerful, even intimidating presence of the fish in life.

Whenever I seen film of Concorde I think of the ray and can picture a shoal like a squadron of these giant kites, their wing edges rippling in undersea flight, a bleakly alien intelligence glowing from the high cockpit of their eyes, the mouth underslung and fitted with the lips of a brutal baby.

Once off the hook, only a thumb-and-finger grip on the nose of the ray will keep you clear of the savage barbs buttoned through its skin.

Ethna, kneeling in the rain to gut and fillet (three stone of fish for the freezer on this occasion), ends up with tender, even lacerated, fingers. Do fish feel pain? My best book on animal behaviour finds itself unable to say. "Pain cannot be defined in an objective, scientific manner," it pleads. "This question is philosophically controversial...We have no empirical means of verifying the theory that animals do have conscious experience similar to ours."

Cold-blooded creatures, one was reared to believe ("poikilothermic organisms" as biology prefers to call them), don't feel the same things we do. Perhaps they feel worse ones, pinned down to the ocean floor for hours by a hook through the lip. A hunter reminded me of this when I objected to his enthusiastic shooting of birds. And the death and dismemberment of the rays, for all their alien aura, are no more defensible than those of grouse or wild geese.

Shoals of fish and flocks of birds have a mystery in common: how do they perform such intricate manoeuvres, such instantaneous changes of direction, as if with a single mind? This is the time of year – in our corner of Connacht, at least – when the first flocks of starlings zoom over the hedge with a swish that puts the heart across man and beast alike. They are not the great sky-darkening migratory flocks of autumn which, in Ted Hughes's image, are like "a bacteria cyclone, a writhing of imps, issuing from a hole in the horizon", but tight-packed flights of a few hundred birds each, terrorising the countryside with their breakneck aerobatics. They sent our pony galloping headlong in his paddock.

A good deal is known, or at least theorised, about the advantages of flocking for birds. It helps to baffle predatory hawks, to give early warnings and to find food. Starlings in flocks can spend more time feeding and less time looking over their shoulders.

But, on the flocks' uncanny abilities to manoeuvre in the air, the experts have a lot less to say.

One of the founders of the modern study of bird behaviour, Edmund Selous, dared to ask if the instantaneous co-ordinations of flight in bird flocks could be due to a form of "thought transference" or "flock brain". But modern research continues to prefer some variation of a follow-my-leader mechanism, served perhaps by the kind of echolocation capacity that bats have.

One researcher has analysed films of flock flight, frame by frame, to claim the sort of corner-of-the-eye co-ordination by which chorus girls keep in step and station. Brian Inglis, who talks about this in his book on "psi" phenomena The Hidden Power (Jonathan Cape), points out that chorus lines are two-dimensional in movement, have a tune to help them and are following a well-drilled choreography. Starlings in a flock have to keep station not only with those ahead and on each side of them, but also with those above and below them, all changing direction unpredictably in a tiny fraction of a second.

November 15th 1986
The new birds of winter

After the gales, each of the stones and shells scattered over the strand stood on its own little pedestal of sand: they had held the grains in place beneath them like paperweights, while the top two inches of the strand dissolved in the wind and hissed away to the dunes.

This is one of the marks of late autumn, like the overlapping ruts of tractors taking shell sand to lime the fields and the compass circles scratched on the dunes by the pointed tips of marram grass. Along the tideline lie clumps of grass and sea pinks snatched from the islands, and among them, big enough to walk around and wonder at, a length of tree trunk, skinned and battered and crusted with gooseneck barnacles. It will make a pair of gateposts for somebody's field, and a piece of coloured twine knotted around it already proclaims it "found".

Down the altered air of this Atlantic shore have come the new birds of winter – solitary, like the redshank at the channel, in flocks, like the golden plover wheeling above the duach, or arriving in relay, like the whooper swans on the far lake.

It suits me to think that the whoopers are flying in directly from Iceland, and certainly the great bugling that goes up with the arrival of each new group – a triumphant fanfare echoing off the cliff, and the excited bowing of heads – is deeply stirring to witness.

But even if the swans have first checked in to Ireland further up the coast, those that arrive at the lake to stay through the winter are likely to be the same birds, year after year – just like the human families who take the same holiday cottage summer after summer. At the famous English wildfowl sanctuary at Slimbridge, in Gloucestershire, some of the Bewick's swans that arrive in winter from Arctic Russia have been turning up there for more than twenty years, each individually recognisable by the pattern of yellow and black on its bill.

One bird, which arrived above the duach the other day, however, was certainly not a regular, pleased as we were to see him – almost, you could say, to feel him, since there is a subtle, electric change in the sky that announces a bird of prey.

The hen harrier – a brown female with a white patch on her rump – was on a tour of the coast, quartering the machair with an attentive, leisurely thoroughness: three or four slow wing beats, then a glide on half-raised wings – more of a bomber than a jet fighter.

I doubted, somehow, that she should be credited with the two or three bird kills I had found along the duach: a lapwing or plover with its head struck off, the breastbone bare of meat, plucked feathers in a trembling arc across the grass – the work of the peregrine falcon is bloodily distinct.

Remarkably, the harrier is sometimes seen hunting in tandem with a peregrine, to their mutual benefit. The peregrine, which makes its kills in the air, stations itself behind and well above the harrier, which makes its kills among birds that "freeze" on the ground.

When the harrier flushes a grouse, say, the peregrine will swoop on it in mid-air. The presence of the peregrine, on the other hand, immobilises more of the small ground-nesting birds, such as pipits and larks, that the harrier favours as prey.

There was a time, indeed, when the harrier found it profitable to hunt in tandem with man – or so some old Irish sportsmen complained in the last century. The bird would hang around, just out of gunshot, until a snipe was downed, and would then dash in and snatch it up before the hunter could reach it. This unsporting behaviour was brought to an end with the invention of the double-barrelled shotgun.

Does the hen harrier harry hens? Very exceptionally, when circumstances permit. But, for at least half its prey, it settles for small rodents or young rabbits, like those that abound on the duach.

The harrier's occasional raids on young grouse helped to bring it close to extinction in these islands. All through the late 1800s it was shot at by dedicated gamekeepers, and its nests among the upland heather were sought out and destroyed. By 1900, only a few pairs survived in Ireland, and in Britain the harrier was pushed to its last refuges in the Hebrides and the Orkneys, where it survived largely on voles.

Only thirty years ago, it was classed by the experts as "a rare straggler" in Ireland, and one which is shot if it remains for any length of time. "Few sportsmen seem capable of sparing these large, slow-flying birds of prey which are so confiding." Since then, however, the harrier's fortunes seem to have turned and there are now probably some 300 pairs that breed in Ireland. The young conifer plantations have given them places to nest and the older State forests offer safe roosting. It is, of course, a protected bird, and thus saved from ending up as a stuffed trophy.

But I find myself wondering how it will get on as the gun clubs pursue their ambition to replenish the Irish moors with grouse. "Birds of prey are not much of a problem," says Prince Philip of the grouse moors at Balmoral. But he would, wouldn't he?

I went after my own winter wild food the other day – mussels from the shore of Killary Harbour. The mussels out on the coast, open to the pounding Atlantic breakers, never grow above a thumbnail in size, but a mile or two up the fjord finds the rocks crusted with prime mussels the length of your finger. In half an hour at low tide, slithering over the weed, I had harvested as heavy a bag as I could carry on my shoulder – and still left scarcely a gap in the dense black masses of shells.

The spread of the mussel rafts on the surface of the Killary offends the eye of some weekenders in the west: they say it spoils the view. They snort at the "beer barrels" which some sea farmers use as a more flexible, storm-resistant way of buoying up a longline of mussel ropes.

Nine winters ago, night classes in mussel farming were held in our local tech, and I wondered in this column if we should one day see the Killary covered from side to side with rafts, like sampans in Hong Kong.

It hasn't happened yet – but if it had kept a hundred young men at home, I think I would have tried to get used to it.

May 16th 1987

Passion in the pond

When the wild white water lily comes to life beneath the water in spring, the leaves it unfurls and pushes up to float on the surface are a beautiful deep crimson; it takes the sun to turn them green.

Such small but delightful revelations are typical of pond proprietorship, now that my plastic-lined hole in the ground is becoming, as they say of gardens, mature. I had certainly not expected the sheer pleasure there would be in the magical resurrection of the water plants, unfolding like Japanese paper flowers from the pool's muddy depths.

Simply by creating a habitat that I have to pass a dozen times a day, a separate little world where life goes on largely irrespective of my scrutiny, I have entered a whole new dimension of the naturalist as peeping Tom.

It is hard, after all, to make much sense of what is going on in a lake or marsh that you have to walk to, and where life is glimpsed obliquely and in scattered moments. But a pond on the way to the vegetable garden, a pond full of novelties brilliantly illuminated by shafts of morning sun – this has the daily compulsion of a wild outdoor aquarium in which nature is free to spring surprises.

The water lilies came from the heart of a marsh above the shore: a slough penetrable only in thigh boots. There the lilies bloom by the hundred in summer, exquisitely indifferent to the fact that no one sees them.

Now, the few transplanted to my pond are already stretching up their buds to the surface and a few weeks will see the flowers open, cradling golden anthers in the whitest, most perfect petals ever made.

The first flowers in the pond have been the marsh marigolds, bright and brassy at the margins. In the middle are the bud spikes of other plants brought home from the lakes last summer: fluffy-flowered bogbean and cheerful pink bistort. Water mint, horsetail, bur reed: one after another this spring, they have pushed their way up through the furry green filaments of algae that shroud and shade the depths.

Some botanists will worry at these thefts from the wild, even of such ordinary marsh plants. In a country with a higher density of garden ponds, the looting of lilies could assume, perhaps, disastrous proportions.

Not only, therefore, do I set a bad example, but might myself fall into the predatory conceit of thinking that some of the rarer plants would be "safer" in my garden than out there in the wild: a naturalist's crime akin to gloating over stolen Rembrandts.

But while my ethics might be flexible in the matter of the lilies, I do not, I am glad to say, feel the least covetous of, for example, the frog orchid, or the marsh helleborine. I know their haunts along the lakes and there they stay.

Along with the plants I "borrowed" from nature came all sorts of organisms, clinging to the stems and leaves, or embedded as eggs or larvae in the mud around their roots.

These have now hatched and multiplied and, joined by winged immigrants from distant waters, have been working out the deadly dispositions of predators and prey.

The savagely carnivorous world of pond life was brought home to me lately by the total disappearance of the tadpoles. A month or two ago I was pleased to find that frogs had discovered my pond and had deposited into its shallows three large dollops of spawn; some 5,000 eggs, say. At this time last year, hatched from frogspawn I had (it seems now, illegally) imported from a hilltop pool, the somewhat bare rim of the brand-new pond was lined with thousands of tadpoles. The fact that, pushed for food, they proceeded to eat each other is beside the point; this year's frogspawn, laid directly, had plenty of nourishment on hand, yet no tadpole is now to be seen.

The creatures I first suspected were the fairly plentiful water boatmen, which fly readily from pond to pond. These strange bugs are like Victorian submarines, all plates and rivets, which row about on their backs underwater, gazing up at the surface film and a rippling silver sky. The bubble of air they carry trapped in their body hairs serves as a buoyancy tank, so that, to rise, they have only to stop swimming.

They will eat almost anything they can successfully attack, so that their sly drift up to the surface among the whirligig beetles, ostensibly to recharge their bubbles, may often hold a lethal intent. The whirligigs, weaving circles around each other on the skin of the water like demented dodgem cars, present inviting if confusing targets. On the other hand, they have two segments to each eye, the lower devoted to underwater surveillance. In all my vigils beside the pond, I have yet to see a whirligig that didn't watch the submarine, oars outstretched, floating up from beneath.

The tadpoles, pursued underwater, may have been easier prey. But a few weeks ago, a new and even more formidable suspect showed itself at the surface: a carnivorous beetle, as big as your thumb, which is capable even of killing the fish in a garden pond, let alone its tadpoles.

The great diving beetle, Dytiscus marginalis, kicks through the water with hair-fringed legs, the sleek shape of its olive brown body superbly streamlined for underwater life. It has so fascinated scientists that one German work, dealing with this insect alone, runs to two volumes and 1,827 pages.

Actually, there is not one great diving beetle in my pond but a pair of them, and every time I have seen them – on three or four occasions over the period of a month – they have been raptly clasped together.

On one occasion, indeed, when we were entertaining some friends from Europe on gooseberry wine beside the pond, the beetles found themselves providing the cabaret, evoking more and more unseemly amusement as the afternoon wore on. Mating Dytiscus will swim together, the male carrying the female, for hours at a time. This sort of behaviour seems not uncommon among pond creatures: think of frogs – only in their case it is the female that carries the male on her back, often for twenty-four hours, and considerable force is necessary to separate them (or so I am told; I should not have the heart to find out).

There might, in fact, have been excellent cause for parting our pair of beetles, because their larvae, fifty millimetres long, will be even more ferociously inclined towards tadpoles than their parents are. (If you are eating breakfast, you should stop here.)

What they do is seize the tadpole in their mandibles (you could go and read Maeve), suck out its juices, pump in a digestive fluid to dissolve the body tissue, and suck it out again (I warned you), leaving only an empty tadpole skin.

One virtue of having water lilies is that you don't need to know what is going on underneath them.

December 19th 1987
Our friends the hares

The sun goes down these evenings behind Tully Mountain across the bay, its smouldering descent framed in my study window. The afterglow is reflected in the river that runs through the strand – a strip of crimson neon in the cold, black sand – and even before it has faded, the stars are glittering like Christmas tree lights in a sky of deepening indigo.

It is not just the spectacle – the bonfire sunset and the bar of crimson light – which pleases me, but the pause of the sunset at this particular notch in the horizon. Next Monday is the winter solstice, and Tuesday will find the sun setting an imperceptible shade further north. By the time it intersects the sea again, between High Island and Inishbofin, we shall be voyaging back towards the spring.

For the moment, though, these still and chilly December nights can fetch me out of the house to stand gazing up at the brilliance of the sky.

There is no canopy of city smoke to dull the stars, no reflection of lights to diminish them. The black silhouette of the mountain cuts off the world to the east, enhancing my illusion of a private view of infinity.

Thus engaged the other evening, I found myself wondering what was happening on a certain hillside at seventy-seven degrees north, much as others might wonder about the winter weather on Ibiza or Crete.

The sky above Germania Land, now at the mid-point of Greenland's winter dark, would be just as crystalline as this, and the silence more total. Around the middle of the day, climbing a hill in twilight and looking south, you might find a faint red streak on the horizon and an answering flush on the snow plain of the frozen fjord. Otherwise, between moons, a scant starlight and perhaps the slow, weaving banners of the northern lights.

Does anything move? A pregnant bear, perhaps, on an outing from her den, or a passing wolf. No foxes, probably: many of those go far out on the pack ice in winter, scavenging hopefully after the bears. But, as they are scattered like furry snowballs among the black shadows of the hill, I should, undoubtedly, meet our friends the hares.

Just four months ago, on my field trip to Greenland, they were playing around our tents in the midnight sun, chewing on yellow poppies like sticks of celery.

Now, in temperatures that weld the very stones to the earth, they have retreated to the bare, windswept ridges between the snow banks, there to feed on withered sedges and twigs of the tiny prostrate willows.

If I had not already been an admirer of hares, this summer's intimate encounters would have made me one.

Where else could you exchange regards, at a hand's stretch, with those "dark, innocent, cold-glazed eyes" that Flora Thompson wrote of? And in these face-to-face communings among the boulders above the camp, only the bulky white fur and a certain stolidity of expression marked out the Greenland hares from those of our hillsides at home.

Both the Irish hare and the "blue" or mountain hare of Scotland are races of the Arctic hare, whereas the common brown hare of Britain arrived from southern Europe long after Ireland had been cut off. Lepus timidus hibernicus has shorter ears than the brown hare, and its tail is entirely white – differences you might need to know in parts of some Ulster counties, where brown hares were introduced for coursing in the last century ("thrush" hares as they're sometimes called in Donegal, because of their speckled coats).

Unlike the Scottish race, which turn almost white in winter, our hares rarely seem to manage much more than a grizzling of grey and a pale patch on the rump. There is no advantage, after all, in turning white where there isn't much snow, and while a certain day length is what triggers a moult for a colour change, the prevailing temperature seems to decide how far the moulting goes.

When Norwegian mountain hares were introduced to France, for example, their descendants took only forty years to settle for a blue-grey winter coat instead of a white one. Even in Scotland, the hares at high altitudes stay white longer than those on the lower moors.

How odd that "timidus" seems, after finding such lack of fear in the hares of our High Arctic hillside. Nothing in their genes spoke of danger in the shape of man. But the hare everywhere is born – unlike the rabbit – with eyes open, fully furred, and almost ready to run, whether from wolves and foxes or men. It stays a light sleeper all its life.

"Being naturally fearful," said that knowing Ulster huntsman Arthur Stringer, "she is never fat." Stringer, writing in the eighteenth century, was an early observer to decide that the zigzag doubling and squatting of the hare was natural, instinctive behaviour – perhaps to make up for its poor forward sight – and not some devilish "craft, subtilty and policy" learned to outwit the hunter.

How flourishing is our hare population and how far is it affected by hunting and coursing? Figures from lushly heathery grouse moors in Scotland (one hare per acre, say, on a few moors in Aberdeenshire) tell nothing about the density in Irish farmland, or on the overgrazed uplands of Connacht.

But hares on the bog around Glenamoy in Co Mayo averaged only one per square kilometre, while the grassland of newly reclaimed bog was positively teeming with them, at forty or fifty per square kilometre. On my own hillside, the hare is much more an animal of rough pasture than of the – now virtually heatherless – heights.

There is far less direct pressure on the hare in Ireland than in England, where, quite apart from the thirty packs of harriers, sixteen packs of basset hounds and eighty-two packs of beagles, the hare is much more intensively shot for food. Until the British banned coursing matches, in 1975, hares were being imported from Ireland.

But neither hunting nor coursing makes much difference to total numbers: countryside that is "emptied" of hares soon fills up again from outside.

"Even hare shoots," writes one English conservation authority, "which may kill many hundreds of animals in a day, only have very temporary effects." As with so many of our animals and birds, how well the hare survives in the long run will depend on what happens to its habitat and to farming practices.

It doesn't catch myxomatosis – in fact, it gained where the rabbit lost – and while it is prey to fox, stoat and mink, the only thing that can catch it when in full flight at 40 miles per hour is the greyhound.

What make park coursing indefensible are not the numbers of hares it kills but its cruelty and its arrogance towards nature.

April 23rd 1988
Learning to love the earwig

Before dawn on one of those astonishing shirt-sleeves days that followed Easter, I switched on the light in the kitchen and hadn't filled the kettle before five brown moths came butting at the window. They were summer size, whirring and furry, and their eyes shone like opals. We inspected each other, nose to nose.

Settling down with a steaming cup to begin writing, I was distracted by the arrival of a new inhabitant of my study, a black weevil maybe half an inch long. He has been around my desk for a week or two, following his snout from Roget's Thesaurus to the word processor and back again, but this time he wandered into the half-open maw of one of those plastic cases that floppy disks come in, and by a well-timed tap on the lid I had him.

His "nose" is, in fact, a boring tool: he has his jaws at the end of it. But he chose to keep them shut, and when I had learned all I could with a magnifying glass I set him at liberty again: Otiorhynchus clavipes, as the book says uninspiringly, with feet like six little ink blots.

And then, after breakfast, I took the hens their feed and, passing the blackcurrant bushes, found their flowers under noisy, fumbling assault by no fewer than four kinds of bumblebee. I stooped over them, trying to memorise the permutations of their football jerseys but, back at the book, was certain only of the simple black-body-orange-tail of Bombus lapidarius. It was not important; I was just trying to get my eye in.

None of it was in the least important, if it comes to that: just three brief episodes, three pauses to be aware of – to be curious about – the lives of species other than my own. My interest is in no way obsessional or systematic: I never shall know the names of all the Irish bumblebees, or call the weevil anything but a weevil.

But, a year or two ago, a weevil was something you tapped out of a ship's biscuit: I had never seen one, let alone knew that there were 500 sorts in these islands alone, all colours and sizes and all with that "prominent rostrum" of a snout.

What has been quite deliberate in my "taking an interest" in insects has been a conscious overcoming of aversion – an aversion drilled into me by a culture which masks its ignorance of invertebrate life with a general distaste for its appearance.

There may well be reasons deep in our genes, instincts inherited from our primate and cave-dwelling past, which generalise from the scorpion and poisonous spiders to instil an avoidance of all insects. We like soft, round-ish, caressable species in some way like ourselves. We warm to behaviour which, however mistaken we may be, seems to relate to our own.

We react especially to postures or actions suggesting parental tenderness: "aah!" we say to the polar bear licking her cubs. And the wildlife we warm to most is what stimulates our own "parenting" responses: chimpanzees, penguins, puppies, baby seals – anything with round head, flat face and big eyes.

"Aah!" is thus wrung out of us by a primal, gene-serving instinct; it is nothing especially tender or noble.

Insects, wearing their skeletons inside out and moving on multiple pairs of legs at an unfamiliar pace, could not seem more alien. Most of the ones we actively dislike are black, colour of night and evil. Ladybirds, butter-flies, bumblebees, dragonflies are redeemed by bright colours; black beetles, however beneficial, are abhorred.

Flying insects "bang into people", betraying their loathsome automatism, but any hint of insect intelligence is seen as uncanny and sinister. Insects cannot win.

Yet a little information can often work wonders. Let us, for example, see what we can do to rehabilitate the earwig, chewer of dahlia petals and denizen of crumpled-up face cloths left hanging on the washing line.

The earwig has been around for close on 200 million years – time enough, one would think, to dispel the notion that it would walk into the ears of sleeping people and there start drilling. The earwig's common names in other European languages suggest the same sort of fear, but none of the Irish names does; even Síle an phíce — Sheelah of the hayfork – is a straightforward folk observation.

When the earwig is resting during daylight hours, it feels safe only in a crevice, with as much of its body as possible in contact with a smooth, dry surface. A rolled-over flower petal or a seed pod offers the perfect refuge.

The "hayfork" forceps at its tail is mainly for defence and will not do more than tickle your finger even if it grips. And tucked away inside the earwig's leathery forewings is another delicate and exquisite pair of wings, quite un-like those of any other insect.

They are pleated like fans and fold across twice to be stowed away – an elaborate performance which is usually too much bother: the earwig prefers to walk.

Two more pieces of information should really make you change your attitude. First, about the earwig's diet. Flower petals sometimes, yes, when other things are in short supply, but also fungi and algae and aphids – up to 100 a day, according to the latest study, which makes earwigs a very useful predator, especially on apples.

But the clincher should be this: the earwig is a caring and responsible mother. For four months of winter, in her nest in the soil, she was brooding over her eggs like a hen, turning them and licking them from time to time to remove the spores of a fungus which might kill them. Now that they are hatched, she is feeding her young and defending them against predators.

There! Have you not misjudged this insect? Could you not bring yourself, as a matter of policy, to repress those automatic gestures of distaste and aggression, those primitive caveperson's responses, and open your mind and curiosity to the teeming invertebrate world? There are perhaps 100,000 species of invertebrate animals in Europe, less than five per cent of which are in any real way offensive to our interests. Without insects there would be no brightly coloured flowers of spring: the colours are to guide not merely bees but myriad sorts of fly. Without insects, too, we should be up to our necks in cow dung, bird shit and dandruff. Mere utility demands that we stop wiping out insect species at the present rate. But a change in attitudes will bring us more: a small, but worthwhile, personal gain in finding harmony with nature.

May 15th 1993

Busy with birds

There were cattle right up on the ridge, a jotting of little black marks along the skyline.

Only a very dry spell would have let them up that high; only a very fine morning would have kept them there, glad of the breeze on both sides of their rocky prominence.

We got out early for a walk, before hills and islands could retreat into anonymous blue haze. There is a special time on these special May mornings when life is balanced perfectly between cool and warm, old and new, past and future – a time when even quite sedate and senior people may feel like walking barefoot on the strand.

Once down the boreen, ahead even of the first tractor, we moved through the zone where sea and land meet with a quite unusual sense of Earth's seamlessness.

There are so many days in winter when the fields seem to stop abruptly at a ragged, hostile boundary; you step across it with your head down.

Today, there was a continuity, a gentle interweaving of terrestrial and marine. As the lambs dozed beside their mothers, lark song drifted out above the fences to find a ready place among the sea sounds on the strand. In the shallows of the channel, a pair of shelduck shared a pool with a merganser – both species with bright vermilion bills, both maritime ducks at home in bays and estuaries.

Every month lights the landscape differently; the sea, too. In May, the sun after breakfast strikes down from the ridge and straight into the breakers, turning them to Venetian glass, turquoise and cobalt. Without a wind, you hear the fall of every drop of gleaming water.

The sun at this angle also makes white things whiter: the ring of foam around a distant rock, the white breast of a diver, the white underparts of razorbills strung out in a flotilla, the spiky whiteness of terns snatching morsels from the skin of the sea.

Some of the terns carried sand eels in their bills, bearing them limply away northwards, to their nesting colony on an islet in a lake behind the shore. At this time, fish may be love tokens, presented by the male birds to their prospective partners.

Such a busy sea. Out beyond the third wave, a flotilla of shags waited on their next bout of hunger.

Cormorants sped back and forth on low and urgent tracks, or posed on offshore skerries with their wings hung out to dry.

At least in the breeding season the cormorant's white thigh patch helps tell it from the shag, even at a distance. Breeding brightens up both birds substantially, enriching the cormorant's black feathers with a glaze of bronze or blue and lighting up the shag's yellow gape and emerald eye, and the metallic green sheen of its plumage.

The shag is now, indeed, rather beautiful; for a few weeks early in the breeding season, it even has a crest. To watch from a clifftop while it swims down after fish is to admire its sinuous ability. (It stays down for a minute, on average.)

But its choice of nest sites in the dankest, darkest corners of cliffs and sea caves, and the hissing one gets for daring to approach its nest of rotting seaweed, make it seem less seabird than sea serpent.

Shags have very fixed ideas about their choice of where to nest, and the Irish birds are very sedentary.

Unlike cormorants, they don't fish in fresh water, or set up breeding colonies on inland trout lakes. Before the Wildlife Act was passed in 1976, there were bounty schemes for cormorants in many parts of Ireland, and thousands of shags were shot in their name at the coastal salmon estuaries.

In the past twenty-five years, the number of shags around Ireland has almost doubled, despite a rising toll of deaths in fishing nets. But very few, if any, of the birds in the "raft" off our strand were actually engaged in breeding this spring. That goes, in fact, for very many of the seabirds one sees around the coast at this time.

Seabirds have a long life and high survival rates. Most of them wait several years before attempting to breed, and they produce few young at a time – one chick per pair from most of the auks (razorbills, guillemots and so on) and perhaps four or five from the shag. Species such as fulmar, puffin and shag sometimes take a year or more off from breeding.

All this is very different from the songbirds of the land, with their brief lives, large broods of young and multiple clutches in the year. And while hedgerow birds are spaced out by territory, the seabirds nesting almost wing to wing along the ledges of the island cliffs seem linked much more directly, in their numbers, to the availability of food and to the impact of disasters.

The population dynamics of seabirds make a fascinating study: the balance of life and death is so fine that changes in the environment affecting adult mortality – such as an oil spill, or overfishing of the sand eel – can produce great swings in numbers.

The proportion of non-breeding birds in a seabird population is also much bigger than among songbirds, and how this is "decided" is still a mystery.

There's a story from the Arctic that, when guillemots leave their islands at the end of the nesting season, they make a great sweep together around the cliffs, to take a rough count of their numbers.

But the real mechanism of population control is likely to be much more complicated, and not quite so romantic.

Recent years

January 2nd 2010
The making of a rare snail

As the year turns, we have to wait for the sun. The mountain looms in its way, so it's well past nine when, as if focused by the fjord beyond, a fierce beam reaches out to gild the islands, one by one, then the edge of the strand, then the spiky fringe of the dunes. Another hour and we're released from Mweelrea's shadow.

Such a crystalline morning took me down to the sands. The softest fall of wavelets underlined a stillness remarked by passing ravens.

They flew above a shoreline ravaged by the autumn clash of swollen river and tide, a maelstrom that swirled around the rocks meant to armour the edge of the fields. Mossy hollows of the dunes still held big, deep ponds, silkily glazed with ice.

The dunes are new, historically, together with their great lawn of machair. A map from 1838 shows the stub of sandhills from which they grew. At the seaward side they are rawly cliffed by storm-driven waves, and within this century they could be gone altogether, the sea reaching in to swallow the lakes behind them.

Even on a beautiful morning, the human rift with nature crouches at the back of the mind.

On a bare and battered strand, December's gentler waves had left crescents of seashells, their bright mosaic crunching underfoot. A thousand limpets at a glance, no two of them the same; myriad bivalves at every scale; snails, clams, pieces of urchin in every colour. I sifted out the usual few to lose in the corners of my pockets – scallop shells the size of fingernails, rosy, orangey, stripy red; one beautifully black.

All the shells had one thing in common: they were built of calcium carbonate drawn from an alkaline ocean. But the pH index of the surface water continues to fall, as the sea absorbs more and more man-made carbon dioxide. Below pH 7 comes acidification. It threatens an unimaginable dissolution of species: not only shellfish, but crustacea, corals, plankton and other vital organisms. This was one of the spectres haunting the Copenhagen climate change conference.

Calcium from the ocean is also, as it happens, key to what is special about the whole ecosystem of Dooaghtry – as the tangle of maritime wilderness below me has been known to generations of ecologists. Powdered into sand from empty seashells and blown inshore across the dunes, the mineral is recycled into land snails of great, sometimes rare diversity.

The new National Biodiversity Data Centre has been taken aback to find the size of Ireland's share of the world's non-marine mollusc species: they thrive in our moist, mild climate.

And the four square kilometres of Dooaghtry are a remarkable land of snails, among the richest in Europe. Seventy species have been recorded here, from the big "garden" snails, sand-blasted blue in their winter niches in the rocks, to creatures no bigger than a match head and invisible in mosses at the edge of the lakes.

Rarest of all is a snail with a shell that at least you can see, almost a centimetre long. And for once, in the heady mix of Latin that bedevils snail appreciation (think of the threatened Vertigo geyeri that attracted Bertie Ahern's derision), it has a decent, even cosy, common name – the sand-bowl amber snail.

Its latest scientific appellation is Quickella arenaria, immortalising the English ophthalmic surgeon and malacologist Hamilton Quick, who discovered it in 1933. This entailed fine dissection to discover, among other idiosyncrasies, an arrow mark at the end of its penis. That helps to mark it out from the rest of the Succineidae, a wetland family with variable but closely similar shells.

Quickella has been lost from three Irish sites, in Offaly and Tipperary, where drainage destroyed its lime-rich habitats at the edges of raised bogs. Dooaghtry is possibly its most important site in the world and a special area of conservation. But the snail's reliance on wet mossy flushes, many less than a metre square, make the hooves of sheep and the random passage of four-wheel-drive vehicles formidable threats to its Lilliput world.

This is the UN's International Year of Biodiversity, and either we care about losing the world's species, however uncharismatic, or we don't. Among them, you know now about the sand-bowl amber snail, a tiny hermaphrodite gastropod with an arrow tattooed on its willy.

January 9th 2010
Hungry birds come calling

The worst of the winter, as I write, has stayed beyond the hill. On this side, shielded from the north and basking in the ocean's glitter, the harsh night frosts are mainly what menace our feathered refugees. Opening the door to another pink dawn, I spark an eruption of redwings from the interior of a big escallonia bush.

They fan away past what is left of the moon, trailing a thin, sighing twitter as they fly to fields along the shore. I can only apologise for the disturbance: all flight costs energy, and flying in alarm even more.

All the birds are now stressed from hunger and wind chill, and millions must already have died across Europe in the massive spilling out of polar cold. Looking back through Another Life, I found the bitter winter of 1985, when "the cats were lining up [redwing] corpses on our doorstep in threes", while others were washed up with dead golden plover along the shore. We no longer keep cats, but at this new year John Sweeney of Achill reported redwings and fieldfares arriving "in clouds" to carpet the island's fields – migrants from Scandinavia pushed west to the edge of Europe.

Redwings are the little thrushes with rufous flanks and a creamy collar and stripe over the eye. Fieldfares are thrushes, too, but bigger, more poised, and affectingly elegant: crisp grey and brown above and a glowing ochre bib. Their flocks keep a distance from people, but redwings have been bouncing in the leaves on our unmown, soggy lawn, stabbing hopefully for worms, and hunger can compel a rare perch at garden feeders.

Just before Christmas we went to the co-op for a hessian sack of peanuts from Argentina, a whole winter's supply, and have already had to dig deep to satisfy our daily dozens of birds.

We like to think that some, at least, are "ours", but know, in reality, that whole successions of tits and finches pass through the garden, some delaying, no doubt, for the food and close shelter.

The house sparrows are ours, I'm sure, for once overwhelmed in a brilliant, squabbling mix of goldfinches and siskins.

A song thrush feeds nervously just beyond the window as I write, fleeing from robins and blackbirds between turns at a box of goose fat and oatmeal.

It is fluffed up beautifully against the cold, and the first flakes of a snow shower lie on her back without melting.

I haven't seen a wren for many days, and that could be bad news. Hunters after spiders, pupae and cocoons, hibernating flies and butterflies, wrens get no special winter help from humans.

They may take over a tits' nest box as a communal roost at night (fifty in one box seems to be the current record). Last February, a reader in Co Antrim sent a photograph of wrens, eight or nine of them, snuggled head down in a swallow's nest in her porch. They've been doing it for years, and the colder it is the more wrens push in. Once they settle, little heads pressed together in the dark and breathing warmer air, no one is allowed to use the front door.

Of all living things, only mammals and birds can maintain a constant body heat no matter how cold the air. For some of the tinier warm-blooded creatures, the extra activity is scarcely worth the trouble. Their large body surface in relation to their size sets up a heat loss that demands a high metabolic rate to burn fuel faster. The colder the winter, the stronger grows the obsessive need for food.

Birds in general have the highest body heat of any animals. Even on a frozen lake, a swan maintains 105 Fahrenheit, or 40.5 Celsius, a temperature which in humans would be fever. A goose will roost on snow if it has to, beak tucked into the warm air beneath the feathers on its back. Birds also warm up the venous blood returning from their extremities by passing it through a coil of warm arterial blood before it reaches the body core.

I wonder how soon Iceland's whooper swans might, given global warming, choose not to bother migrating to Ireland for the winter.

January 16th 2010

Birds captured in portrait

"The frosty carpal bar, broad 'thin as paper' wings, all-dark underwings, and sticklike dangling legs. Sweet Mother of God, this was it – the first live Wilsons seen off Ireland…" Fifty miles out in the Atlantic from southwest Cork, a trawlerload of young birders on a "pelagic" excursion leaped to pour a barrel of chum – oily, rancid fish scraps – into the sea, to lure the little petrel into staying within camera range.

The passion of the dedicated, travel-anywhere birder and his ecstatic rewards (it is almost exclusively a male pursuit) seem fitting topics for a new year in which any escape to the natural world must have a lot going for it. And a new book by an archetypal devotee gives both a brilliant understanding of the calling and many good reasons for showing it better respect. "I'm supposed to be fair game for those who wish to poke fun at me for being eccentric," writes Anthony McGeehan, regretting the media's reach for the term "twitcher", thus alienating him from a multitude "unbrushed by the wings of natural history".

McGeehan is warden of the nature reserve on Belfast Lough, thronged in winter with flocks of migrant Arctic waders. He is also a gifted photographer, patient sound recordist and engaging storyteller.

In Birding from the Hip (from the Sound Approach, with two CDs clipped inside the cover), he collects and illustrates the best of his (often very entertaining) columns for birding magazines, and also narrates them on the CDs for bedtime listening, with music and relevant bird calls.

The book also holds delightfully waspish contributions by his wife, Maireád, a classic birding widow and mother. Her husband is supposed to pay for his obsessions and trips away with the lads by doing the hoovering and washing-up and spending time with the children, a bargain not always adequately fulfilled.

She dreads the excited phone messages that whisk him away to distant rarities, especially when she jots them down wrongly. ("Ring Bill Gull in Belmullet" was Ireland's first ring-billed gull; he nearly missed it.)

A group photograph of a score of "the lads", drawn to a rocky slope of Cork's Mizen Head by the sighting of an isabelline wheatear, rather confirms the stereotype: anoraks, woolly caps and telescopes on tripods.

They all look supremely happy, even before the pub, brimming with technical expertise and the thrill of ticking another rarity for their life lists, and the camaraderie shines out, too.

Just where birding shades into ornithology – the exacting scientific knowledge of birds, their distribution, populations and behaviour – is sometimes hard to know. McGeehan's passion for watching birds began "on the cusp of my teens", when a pair of wellingtons were what he most wanted for Christmas. But even latecomers to birding become skilled in marshalling details that identify storm-swept autumn waders or warblers from North America, or a vagrant wagtail from Siberia paddling in a puddle on the coast of Donegal.

Birding from the Hip is hip indeed to birds with a "split supercilium", "a hint of rufous on the scapulars" or even "semi-palmations between the toes", but McGeehan insists "it's not what it looks like, it's how it makes you feel". He writes of America's hermit thrush as "a little gall of a bird with a kind eye and a rusty tail [and] such a song that, when the bird stopped singing, you felt like whispering Amen". His photographs are of exceptional quality.

As a bird's name, that of a blacktailed godwit may not impress, but one turns the page to his portrait of the wader, taken at Belfast a couple of springs ago, with a gasp at sheer beauty.

In the modern eruption of Irish birding, the exquisite close-up images made possible by telescopic digital photography have been matched by work of painters such as Killian Mullarney and Michael O'Clery. And birds have continued to inspire outstanding Irish sculptures such as those, in gleaming metal, by the late Conor Fallon.

Among my presents at Christmas came a curlew carved in wood by Norman Styles at his workshop in Grangecon, Co Wicklow. His sculptures are shaped from fallen timber found in local demesnes or native woodlands and "given life again", as he says, under his chisel. Thus, my curlew has plumage curved to the grain of walnut, sleek and caressable, a bill of dark bog oak from Kerry, and a base of golden yew from Grangecon Demesne itself: a companionable bird of imposing presence and grace.

February 20th 2010
Man versus root

The frosts have laid the hillside low, powdering the bracken, bleaching the rushes and combing the grasses into cowlicks of limp straw. But gardeners of the food-rearing sort can welcome a winter that takes a proper toll of aphids and allied pests, and crumbles lumpy soil into that ideal state for sowing, the "fine tilth" that all the books demand.

Frost has also levelled the weeds, but not done anything to weaken the hidden networks of their roots. On my knees to rehabilitate a long-neglected vegetable bed, I felt a rush of sympathy for the host of new allotmenteers breaking fresh ground in their first spring outdoors.

Back at our own beginnings, I set out grasping the handlebars of a powerful rotavator. Like some wild animal, it bucked and roared, snorting clouds of exhaust fumes as it churned into the stony soil. It was quickly abandoned in favour of a peaceful, contemplative spade, but not before it had sown half the field with self-generating fragments of marsh woundwort.

This tall, crowding herb stores up its energy reserves in underground stolons like long, white cigars. They shatter at a touch, each little piece to grow anew.

Marsh woundwort is an unlikely suburban weed, but I share the more familiar cabling of couch grass, Elymus repens. Its slender white hawsers just ask to be hauled from the soil, but for every exultant moment when a root delved for, foot after foot, surrenders itself intact, a host of struggles end in a mere snap, and whatever is left will sprout again.

The quickest, easiest, non-organic answer is to spray with glyphosate. A glimpse of what arable farming was like before herbicides is in John Stewart Collis's classic memoir, The Worm Forgives the Plough. "You cultivate the field," he wrote, "drag it, chain-harrow it, pulling up enough couch to build a rick which you then burn in bundles and lines. But you can get more up – and then more. I refuse to use space in writing about it…"

But roots can get interesting, even in their great variety. I fight the claws that emerge from the end of the creeping buttercup's shoots, or that anchor the tips of arching briars with a back-wrenching grip. I burrow after dark fronds of horsetail root, in the full futility of tackling a herb that can penetrate for twenty metres, releasing little cluster bombs of tubers at any attempt to haul it up. And then there are the deep, brittle fangs of tap-rooting perennials I introduced myself: ineradicable Russian comfrey, and the horseradish we will never be without.

We know that roots draw in food and water for the plant and give it firm anchorage. But research into the rhizosphere (the area immediately around the roots) is showing it to be busy with two-way traffic – indeed, multiple interlinkages between roots and the rest of the life of the soil: its microbes and myriad other organisms, as well as the roots of other plants.

More than eighty per cent of land plants, for example, have roots that depend on a partnership, or symbiosis, with tiny fungi called mycorrhiza. These supply inorganic nutrients from the soil in exchange for carbon from the plant's photosynthesis.

The carrot is just one plant that exudes a substance from its hairy roots to trigger the fungal growth around them. Indeed, such exudates are thought to spark all kinds of interactions between plants and soil organisms, or between one kind of plant and another.

"Companion planting" has been a long-running refinement of the organic movement, drawing on traditional experience, on folklore and sometimes on rather dodgy science. Some plants seem to grow better together, others definitely don't; some plants attract helpful insects, others repel pests. The more science learns about plants' strategies for survival, and their hidden interlinkages, the sooner we shall know whether companion plantings that are "said to" work really do.

The beneficial companionship of carrots and onions, to hide the smell of carrots from the dreaded carrot fly, is an old favourite (I prefer to use Bionet to keep the pest out), but this advice is also strong on introducing native wild plants to the allotment to attract companionable and beneficial insects – yarrow, for example, to bring insects to control aphids on the broccoli (not, it could be said, until the yarrow starts blooming in July).

Native hedges to bring birds to eat the snails and caterpillars are fine if there's space for them, which adds point to the association's plea for bigger local authority allotment plots. Forty square metres, apparently the current trend, is about the size of one modest polytunnel.

March 6th 2010
How do I feel about hunting?

A fox left its mark on one of my freshly dug vegetable beds the other night, stitching its track across the frosty soil. It reminded me how long it has been since I actually saw one of these animals. At latest estimate, there could be some 90,000 foxes in Ireland, but there are undoubtedly more roaming Foxrock, Dublin's garden suburb, than survive on the sheep-farming hillsides around Thallabawn.

How do I feel about hunting, of foxes or anything else? As a wimp who sold his new shotgun because the bang was so shockingly loud, I was clearly never cut out for that side of country life. The first fox I ever saw close up was writhing in an ancient gin trap, and I was left to hit it hard. Another fox killed all our hens one night and hid them up the hill.

There will be lampers abroad in the next few weeks, as lambing approaches, mimicking the vixen's mating invitation with a squeal of polystyrene rubbed across a windscreen, sweeping the hillside with the spotlight and not always remembering that it's illegal to fire a gun from the roadside window of a 4x4.

A farmer friend in Sligo once lost more than 100 lambs, all taken from twins, and such experience has to be set against the sometimes glib, green view of foxes as natural cullers of a "doomed surplus" of weak and sickly lambs, or mere scavengers of afterbirth.

So where does that leave me and fox hunting, with horses, dogs and hallooing? "Any man who is utterly unconcerned" with foxhunting, said Lord Dunsany, "lives a little apart from the rest of us."

And so do I, both geographically and culturally. But as an ex-Brit, I found the prolonged and vehement polarisation of English society over the banning of foxhunting with dogs an ugly and wounding affair with a largely futile outcome. The death of a fox in a hostile countryside is rarely anything but grisly, and if farmers are prepared to put up with the heavy brigade charging across their ditches and fences (some, it should be said, are not), I am not passionately disposed to object.

As a naturalist, I try not to confuse issues of cruelty with those of conservation. While discovering that a move from city to country does not automatically make one a hunter, my concern with the death or persecution of wildlife springs mostly from ecology – whether shooting, for example, threatens the number of woodcock or grouse, or simply substitutes one kind of death for another, quite natural mortality.

I believe the shooters who say they love nature. They tend to know a great deal more than I do about some parts of it, and often help to preserve habitats that benefit wildlife as a whole.

Anglers, too, are generally a force for conservation, except when they infest our waterways with invasive alien species.

None of this means I personally approve of hare coursing, even of the recent, muzzled kind, or that I think the proposed banning of the Ward Union stag hunt would be any kind of assault upon "country sports" traditions or the rural way of life. This is where animals of no competition with human interest, or economic value as food, are terrified for entertainment in a highly contrived event. (The red deer is one owned by the hunt, carted to the start, released for the chase on horseback, with dogs, and eventually recaptured to run again another day.)

For almost a century, from 1854, the Ward hunt had the freedom of farmland northwest of Dublin. Most of Meath was under grass. The hunt fielded, at times, much more than 100 riders, many of them British and Irish army officers. (Indeed, by Eric Craigie's account in his An Irish Sporting Life, some officers on leave early in the second World War leaped so recklessly at Meath's high, double-ditched fences that horses were killed, and the livery stables refused to hire out more.)

In post-war Ireland, the advance of tillage, barbed wire, stud farms, commuter housing and schools has steadily circumscribed the running of the deer in, as Craigie wrote, a "country given to stag hunting".

An end to the hunt in its present form, and the arbitrary inclusion of hunt kennels in new legislation on dog breeding, both proposed by Minister John Gormley, is the focus of a protest campaign that has gathered in sixteen organisations, ranging from the Hunting Association of Ireland to the Irish Hawking Club.

RISE! – Rural Ireland Says Enough! – an offshoot of Countryside Alliance Ireland supported by the Irish Farmers' Association, says the new proposals "represent part of a wider, fundamentalist Green agenda being foisted on people".

With such a goad to rural paranoia, they'll probably go a long way.

March 20th 2010

Where blackbirds dare

Why do blackbirds think I want to murder them? Of all the birds that come to the box of oatmeal on my study window sill, Turdus merula is the biggest and most aggressive, bullying even the song thrush, yet its eye must not catch mine across the word processor or it's off. As for opening the front door, away it whirrs under the hedge, screeching in shock and alarm.

There are, as I shall be told by readers, quite other blackbird experiences – birds that are called to be fed from the hand, or that bring their young into the house each year to have their picture taken on the kitchen mat (both in Mark Cocker's Birds Britannica).

But their generally highly strung behaviour is undeniable. Even St Kevin, with his arm stuck out the window at Glendalough, must have been waiting for hysterics to erupt from the bird nesting on his palm. ("Are his fingers sleeping?" wondered Seamus Heaney. "Does he still feel his knees?") More to the point ecologically in a rigorous winter, with every scrap of food hard earned, is the cost in energy of such superfluous alarm.

Needless fright is also common among the little birds that flee our nut-feeders on any human approach. Cats, stoats, foxes – all these could mean predatory harm, but big people in fluffed-up coats and woolly hats? It is, after all, some time since anyone put a pie crust over four-and-twenty blackbirds, even for Come Dine With Me.

Blackbirds brought their terror from the forest floor: look how they rummage, scattering fallen leaves – or oatmeal – in all directions with one beady eye on the shadows. In Britain, as late as the mid-nineteenth century, the blackbird was still a bird of woodland and unknown as a nesting bird near houses. In Ireland it was dispossessed of woods far earlier, adapting to gardens, farmland and hedgerows and even to the virtually treeless islands of the west.

That fear of humans had to be acquired was certainly Charles Darwin's belief. He wrote how, on the virgin Galapagos, "I pushed a hawk off a tree with the muzzle of my gun, and the little birds drank water out of a vessel which I held in my hand." Many naturalists have noted how, in long-inhabited countries, the most timid of birds adapted quickly to roaring monsters of trains or new motorways, but flew from any human figure on the skyline.

In changed times, do they never unlearn their fear? An American team recently published Stress and the City: Urbanization and Its Effects on the Stress Physiology in European Blackbirds. They hand-raised urban and forest-living blackbirds under identical conditions and "tested their corticosterone stress response" every few months. The city birds had a lower stress response than their arboreal cousins. Such adaptation, the team suggested, may be ubiquitous among wildlife in towns.

In Spain, three ecologists produced a recent paper: To Run or to Fly: Low Cost Versus Low Risk Escape Strategies in Blackbirds. It was based on "simulated predator attacks" on blackbirds in four wooded parks in Madrid. The researchers – with permits – advanced on the ground-foraging birds at a steady speed of one metre per second (whether they waved their arms isn't stated) and noted the distances at which they ran, or flew, and how far they went.

From 203 such sorties they concluded that blackbird decisions on whether to run or fly depend on when they choose to escape, and that if they fly, which takes more energy, they go further – all of which makes sense. Juvenile blackbirds flew more often, perhaps for fear of making the wrong choice, and adults flew more often in the afternoon, when they are heavier from feeding, choosing more rapid safety at greater cost in energy.

Blackbirds, often solitary, can make up their own minds – but how do flocks of birds avoid wasting good feeding time by false alarms from fidgety and watchful individuals? A British team, led from Oxford University, sought "evidence for a rule governing the avoidance of superfluous escape flights" by lengthy videoing of the behaviour of flocks of redshank as they were attacked by sparrowhawks – or not, as the case may be – at a salt marsh in Scotland.

In one study of more than 900 alarm flights, more than three-quarters of them were unnecessary: the approaching bird was not a predator, or there was no apparent cause for alarm.

But, still, one rule of thumb became clear. Departure of a single bird might rouse some curiosity (the redshank has no alarm call), but only the simultaneous flight of a number of birds would trigger immediate response from the flock.

Like the blackbird, they clearly spend a lot of time – and energy – getting things wrong.

March 27ᵗʰ 2010
My wild primroses

In the thicket of bare willows beyond our hedge, the lower twigs fly wisps of fleece dragged from the backs of foraging sheep: they shimmer in the sun like Tibetan prayer flags. On this side, on mossy ground quite frost-shorn of last year's weeds, a few clumps of primroses gleam, for once unchallengeably prima rosa.

The clear and singing lemon-yellow of the primrose, so strangely full of light, moved the poet Gerard Manley Hopkins to one of his special coinages. "Take a few primroses in a glass," he mused in his journal, "and the instress of – brilliancy, sort of starriness: I have not the right word – so simple a flower gives is remarkable. It is, I think, due to the strong swell given by the deeper yellow middle."

But scientists have given more obsessive attention to the primrose than any poet. What put Darwin down on his (often tender) stomach on the lawn, transferring fertilising pollen from flower to flower, was the classic demonstration by Primula vulgaris of floral dimorphism: two different forms of the same flower, each on separate plants, designed to help ensure outbreeding in fertilisation

The first wild primroses to bloom in my garden are growing below hawthorn hedges more than thirty metres apart. Picking a few from each colony of flowers and inspecting them closely, I found them conveniently illustrating the point. While superficially identical, the flowers on one side of the garden were "pin-eyed"– on the other, "thrum-eyed".

In the first kind, the male stigma sticks up to the top of the flower's tube, with the female anthers in a ring lower down. In the second, those positions are reversed, and each flower conjures different size of pollen. The result is that insects with long tongues, such as bumblebees, moths and butterflies, when reaching for the nectar at the bottom of the tube, cross-pollinate each kind of flower to produce the biggest and best seed crops. "I do not think anything in my scientific life has given me so much satisfaction," wrote Darwin, "as making out the meaning of the structure of these plants."

Getting this sorted might seem the end of the primrose's fascination for science, but the study of "reciprocal herkogamy" has forged ahead in population genetics. Counting how many of each kind of flower there are has been a basic undertaking, and I was fascinated to Google a paper in 1938 by Britain's JBS Haldane, a famously controversial communist scientist and intellectual bogeyman of my youth. He spent time counting hundreds of "pins" and "thrums" in the woods of Wales and southern England to see how nearly equal their numbers might be. The answer: pretty equal, as in any well-ordered society.

April 24th 2010
Flight of the doves

A new voice in the garden's dawn chorus offers a thoughtful counterpoint to the sharper trills of the morning, a meditative mantra drifting from the shadows at the top of the tallest Lawson's cypress: ku-koo-ku, ku-ku. When the male gets going in early spring, with his bigger voicebox and operatic thrust, the call can deceive.

"I've heard the first cuckoo!" came emails in March, but, no, it was the collared dove.

Streptopelia decaocto arrived a few years ago in a neighbour's conifer shelterbelt down the boreen. The male's spirited flight display, with a clap of the wings, carved a new shape in the sky, and at least three broods of young a year guaranteed our eventual annexation.

The little clump of Lawson's are the only "urban" trees on the acre, growing bigger, perhaps, than would suit in Stillorgan, and offering the doves dense foliage from which to mob an over-inquisitive magpie. Their excitement call on such occasions is, as one of my big bird books puts it, "a nasal-sounding, swearing 'rrah'" – enough, anyway, to fetch me out of the polytunnel to see what was going on. One doesn't expect swearing from such poised and elegant birds.

They have such refinement of proportion, and a warm colour that finds grey at its most beautiful. (A little black and white medal ribbon at the neck is the "collar".) Moving gracefully side by side, pecking up fragments of nut below the feeders, the doves are also, unmistakably, un-Irish.

That's hard to say now, when they're pretty well everywhere – and always somewhere new. The past eighty years has seen the dramatic expansion through Europe and America from the doves' ancient heartland in India.

There, they range through dry, cultivated country dotted with groves of trees and farm clusters, and they still like to settle somewhere with a mix of peaceful open space, trees and benevolent buildings (wires, too, for perching on). Most small towns and villages in Ireland, and many suburbs, seem to fit the bill.

The doves arrived here in 1959, spotted first in Galway, and are now counted by BirdWatch Ireland as one of Ireland's top twenty most widespread garden birds.

But population estimates are still vague – 20,000 to 100,000 breeding pairs, says one international estimate, which seems safe enough, or the 30,000 territories, estimated "by extrapolation" from Britain's 200,000, in the atlas of breeding birds published in 1993.

Now there's a new atlas in gestation for these islands – Bird Atlas 2007-2011 – for which the third season of fieldwork has just begun. With the British Trust for Ornithology at the helm, BirdWatch Ireland is co-ordinating volunteers for patrols of their local "tetrad" (a three-kilometre-by-three-kilometre square). When results are in, the true spread of the collared dove should be revealed.

As I write, in mid-month, the authentic cuckoo has not made itself heard in the land, though a sudden and wonderful lurch into spring makes it feel imminent.

The return to our changing climate could play ducks and drakes (so to speak) with the cuckoo's timing. There are teasing problems in studying the earlier spring arrival in Europe of such trans-Saharan migrants. A German ornithologist, Arie van Noordwijk, set out three explanations. It could be that the departure time from Africa has not changed, but migration through Europe has speeded up. Or the birds might leave earlier because the seasons in Africa are also changing. Or the climate in Africa has not changed but natural selection has changed the cues that send the birds on their way.

A more controversial option has come from an Italian research duo, Nicola Saino and Roberto Ambrosini. They propose that the migrants may be able to predict meteorological conditions on their breeding grounds.

"This seems puzzling," they admit. But finding links between seasonal temperature changes in Europe and Africa persuades them that a "climatic connectivity" may give the birds "a clue to predict meteorological conditions". To judge by this spring's arrival of swallows in an Ireland shivering from winter and almost totally lacking in flies, they can still get it wrong.

Collared doves have inspired their own field of study, not least in how fifty birds from the Netherlands, escaping from a pet breeder in Nassau and reaching Florida, have swept the species north and west, threatening America's smaller native doves. (Arizona is just one state with an official shoot-on-sight policy.) The last of our own rock doves, slaty-blue ancestors of city pigeons and the wildest of our Columbidae family, will continue to keep out of the way, on the more remote cliffs and islands of the west.

May 29th 2010

A goldfinch's love song

As trees grow tall on the acre and their canopies merge in a blur of green and gold, the bird life grows suddenly richer, if sometimes elusive. The real cuckoo came, morning after morning, to perch somewhere on the wire just beyond the nesting collared doves and mock their imitations with its call – but as for spotting it through the leaves, not a hope. I knelt in the tunnel, weeding and planting out, while it yodelled over my head.

Other voices on the acre are excitingly new, freezing me to the spot. From the top of the ESB pole, a cock mistle thrush rasps and chatters into the morning – a challenging, wide-beak utterance, nothing so sweet as the song thrush delivers. Even harsher, if far more inventive, is the torrent of sound from the little sedge warbler, roused by magpies from a nest beneath the willows.

But my warmest surprise has been the song of paired goldfinches from the ash beside the house. To have these brilliant birds – Ireland's parakeets – at one's feeders through the winter is a delight in itself. But they breed late in spring, laying eggs between mid-May and early August, so that having them around the garden while the thrushes and tits are nesting is no firm promise of residence. Even as our male took up his territory, I met a little flock of his fellows skipping away down the boreen.

His sweet, chirruping jingle was delivered while swivelling on his perch like one of those little clockwork toys you see on Antiques Roadshow. He was answered by his mate from a twig across the tree, an unusual bond of song. The birds flew off together, to a patch of grass we call a lawn. They fed on soft dandelion seeds, pulling them from swollen buds and scattering the silk.

A German biologist studying "seed preference and energy intake of gold-finches Carduelis carduelis in the breeding season" found (don't ask me how) that a male goldfinch consumes more oxygen feeding on dandelion and coltsfoot seed heads than when fed on loose, dry seeds.

Well, gosh, work does need oxygen. But it takes this reductive kind of science to tackle simpler wonderings. Some of mine are about colour in nature. Humans love bright colours for no very obvious reason. But the colours we see in nature are not the same as other species perceive them. Bees and birds, for example, can see different or extra colours because their eyes are sensitive to ultraviolet light and ours are not. Blue tits use ultraviolet reflectance in choosing mates; kestrels see colour in rodent scent marks on the ground. Some biologists argue that ecologists whose studies depend on human perceptions of wild colour may be wasting a lot of their efforts.

How goldfinches see each other's bright red masks and yellow wing flashes I haven't yet discovered. But the origin of both is in carotenoids, the organic pigments produced in plants. Googling found a bird breeder who feeds his caged goldfinches everything from red roses and tomatoes to pomegranates and cayenne pepper to help keep their faces red.

June 5th 2010

The willows in the wind

Such a flowering! Such white waves of hawthorn breaking over the ditch, such singular billows of burnet rose on the high bank of the boreen.

In the garden, too, a broom bush suddenly twice the size, a golden fountain in our faces.

Shrub roses voluptuously perfect, the one from Tibet, Rosa moyesii, waving tall wands of crimson. A long time ago, fogbound in a tent in Greenland, I promised myself a few roses at home as a change from cabbages and turnips: this was much what I dreamed.

In the midst of all the splendour, on the sunniest, calmest days of late May, the big goat willow in the Hollow decided to shed its seeds. By big I mean as big as it gets, ten metres high and wide every way, a dozen stems curving out to fill the corner where the stream swings under the hedge. Their elbows rest on the opposite bank, the better to round out its shape. Nowhere else on the hillside could it possibly exist, so safe from people, their cattle and the worst of storms.

Where its branches swoop up from the Hollow the willow's canopy becomes

69

an intimate view from the window, cheering us in early spring as bumblebees throng its flowers; thereafter for willow warblers flitting and singing, and tits hanging upside down for aphids under the leaves.

The tree is, however, female, in an unmistakable way. Most catkin-bearing trees have catkins of both sexes growing on the same tree, but in willows only a female tree can bear female flowers, fruits and seeds.

Its catkins become upright, thumb-sized sausages of fluff in which each silky hair connects with infinitesimal seeds. And a tree in full fruiting vigour, such as ours this May, disappears behind a billion-strong surge of progeny clothed in cotton wool. They are pollinated by wind and insects from the bright golden catkins of the numerous male "pussy" willows.

Unlike most other willows, Salix caprea will not grow from a length of branch pushed into moist ground – it depends on its seeds for reproduction.

Its best weather genetically is thus a good ocean gale to carry its seeds for kilometres, followed by a downpour to embed them in any likely patch of bare soil. They germinate almost immediately, as if to some secret assessment of odds. So our tree was limiting its chances by letting go in such fine, calm weather.

For days on end a slow blizzard of silk drifted across the acre, lodging seeds in cobwebs and crevices, sometimes in my hair and ears. Even in still air a seed can take ten seconds to fall a metre. (The things they study!) Below the tree itself, whole catkins have fallen, carpeting the grass in giant cotton buds and drifting away in the stream. It has all been memorably profligate, and as the year wears on I shall be pulling up tough-rooted seedlings from flower pots, seed trays, drystone walls, the crack beside the doorstep.

"Goat" came from its use as fodder for the animal, a lowly term lost in posher garden forms of the species, such as the weeping Kilmarnock (a male clone and better behaved). To most country people the only distinction between "sallies" is – or was – between osiers and the rest: the ones from which you could weave a turf creel, lobster pot or potato basket and those you couldn't. In most townlands of the west and on the islands there's what's left of a bed of Salix viminalis or Salix purpurea, small osiers that were coppiced for such ends.

But botanists can sort out about thirty kinds of willow growing in Ireland.

The tree that reached here naturally in perhaps six or seven forms has been added to by introductions and hybrids between the species.

Indeed, with such frequent crossings it's hard to know why the core species have kept so distinct from each other.

In the one little streamside thicket of willows that shelters my potatoes are four quite separate kinds of tree, all different in height and habit, leaf shape and colour.

Perhaps, through blessed isolation and prevailing winds, we are spared the plague of fungal rust that overtakes most of the west's goat willows by late summer, browning and curling the leaves at waysides and ditches far inland.

It's a miserable sight and looks like drought, but it isn't. A forester friend once showed me a brassy willow beetle that can do a lot of damage, but that's not it either.

Blame something called Melampsora, a worldwide family of pathogenic rusts with at least twenty species of its own.

Melampsora is the main disease of willows grown as bioenergy crops and thus newly under the microscope.

Genotypes bred for resistance seem to be the answer commercially, but the wayside, streamside sallies of the west will be left to their own defences. I wonder if, without the rust, they might all be twice the size.

June 12th 2010

The ocean blooms

I grew up in a landscape carved almost entirely from chalk. At the eastern fringe of Brighton, on the Sussex coast, white cliffs reared up at the bottom of the street. Behind us rose the first curve of the South Downs, its crest still a chalky rubble of wartime ploughing. I scaled the cliffs to pick clove-scented stocks growing wild in the cracks, fished prawns in chalky runnels of the lower shore and brought home big, wave-rolled chunks of chalk to carve with my father's chisels.

All this rose to mind with last week's photographs from space of great turquoise swirls in the ocean west of Ireland – a milky bloom of plant plankton (phytoplankton) of the species Emiliana huxleyi.

Such blooms are not unusual in early summer, as nutrients rising from the seabed feed phenomenal reproduction of single-celled algae, the primary "grass" of the ocean's food chain. When conditions are right, the special gleam of Emiliana can develop simultaneously across 100,000 square kilometres of sea – yet each individual cell is no more than some four thousandths of a millimetre in diameter.

There are thousands of species of phytoplankton, but what gives Emiliana its sequin-like sparkle is the cell's secretion of chalky platelets (coccoliths), a beautifully intricate armour revealed by the electron microscope. The function of these little sun-reflecting shields of calcium carbonate is unknown – perhaps as filters against ultraviolet rays, or help in buoyancy. But collectively, drifting to the ocean floor, and raised in geological upheavals, their substance helped to build up the strata of chalk that band the cliffs of Antrim and built the snowy ramparts of the white cliffs of Dover – and those at the bottom of my street.

Thomas Henry Huxley, Darwin's pugnacious champion, was the nineteenth-century biologist recognised in Emiliana huxleyi, having studied the deep mud dredged up in explorations for transatlantic cable-laying and finding coccoliths – his word – composing so much of it. "A great chapter of the history of the world is written in the chalk," he wrote; and now its living organisms are under study for another great chapter, that of anthropogenic climate change.

Emiliana has its own website, soes.soton.ac.uk/staff/tt/, at which "Ehux" (some call it Emily) is discussed by marine scientists in enthusiastic, and not overly technical, detail, with pictures and maps. This shining star among organisms so vital to ocean life, not to mention the future of human comfort, deserves the widest audience.

In comments on the photographs of the Emiliana bloom, Joe Silke of the Marine Institute saw it as a particular sign of ocean health, as the plankton's photosynthesis generates oxygen both in the sea and for the atmosphere.

But its climatic significance is even wider. The shimmering armour that makes the blooms of coccolithophores so obvious reflects light and heat back out into space rather than warming the ocean. One satellite study found an annual area of blooms covering 1.4 million square kilometres. And the algae's mass manufacture of coccoliths from calcium and carbon adds to the ocean's seabed store of carbon and affects the amount of carbon dioxide held in the atmosphere.

Along with other phytoplankton, Emiliana produces the gaseous compound dimethylsulphide. Some of this, after the cells die or are eaten by the tiny animals of zooplankton, rises up from the sea in aerosol particles.

These become nuclei for droplets of water condensation that make clouds. Their whiteness (albedo), as we are learning, also helps the planet to reflect sunlight back into space. Blooms of Emiliana in the northeast Atlantic have produced concentrations of dimethylsulphide up to ten times higher than in the surrounding waters.

Such important actions of phytoplankton in taking carbon out of the atmosphere and otherwise regulating climate have encouraged experiments in promoting blooms by fertilising tracts of ocean with the trace element iron. It could work, but, like so many strategies proposed for "geoengineering", it takes science into unknown hazards.

This spring brought proof from Canada that iron enrichment sharply increases the chances of producing blooms of highly toxic plankton species, such as those constantly monitored by our Marine Institute for their threat to aquaculture and coastal ecosystems.

The build-up of man-made carbon dioxide could menace Emiliana itself.

What normally erases a bloom of the cells, along with consumption by zooplankton, is attack by the ocean's teeming viruses and bacteria. But, like all marine organisms drawing on calcium for their structures – everything from crabs and winkles to coral reefs – coccolithophores are at hazard from the progressive acidification of the sea.

"It is by the population of the chalk sea," wrote Thomas Huxley in 1868, "that the ancient and the modern inhabitants of the world are most completely connected." This early support for evolutionary theory carries even more resonance today.

June 26th 2010

No moisture for Mayo

Like ghosts an old underpainting, tawny shades of drought have been creeping across the hillside, sketching in the ribs of rock and hummocks of glacial gravel so shallowly skimmed with grass. By Midsummer's Day we were longing for the showers that even the winsome weatherpersons on TV no longer dared to call a risk.

For half a year we have watched the rain passing us by on the weather maps, leaving this corner of Mayo largely high and dry. Until the first tentative skifts of drizzle edged in from the Atlantic this week – a mere thickening of the atmosphere – our "moisture deficit" was close to Belmullet's 37 millimetres.

This would fill almost four times the calibrated measuring glass, a long crystal condom that I take to the rain gauge in the lawn each morning, noting the amounts for Met Éireann's benefit.

Usually, 10 millimetres is a good wet day. In the six months to Midsummer's Day the total was 312.2 millimetres, compared with last year's 539.1 millimetres and the 707.2 millimetres of 2008 (which was, indeed, a bit much).

We still take our water by gravity feed from the hill stream. A long pipe finally wriggles in behind an immovable boulder to rest in a crevice of the shallow pool above. The stream itself has dwindled to a single shadowy thread, ducking under rocks for metres on end and barely uttering a tinkle on its way from the bog to the sea.

The pool, which you could almost cover with your doormat, drains out through a gap between the grassy bank and the boulder, a gap choked with cobbles of various size. Improving this "dam", I note from the column's archive, has been an enterprise of droughts reaching back to the 1980s. This year's technological advance was to tie each little sod of turf (carved from the bank with a penknife) into a plastic freezer bag before working it into any likely-looking hole between the rocks. Plasticine might have done a better job.

Meanwhile, we balance the trickle into the pool with our domestic needs far below and take the washing-up water out to wet the potatoes – a microcosmic reminder that, as the climate changes, much of Ireland's commercial potato-growing may have to come to an end.

The words "moisture deficit" began to creep into the weather bulletins this week, as it became clear that a few showers from the Atlantic were unlikely to offer what was needed. Seeking definition, I consulted Met Éireann's website. Soil moisture deficit is the term for the amount of rain needed to bring the soil back to its "field capacity" (or, as the website adds helpfully, "the maximum water a pot plant can be watered and not leak water"). In the model developed for Ireland, the 37 millimetres that Belmullet lacks is the deficit for well-drained soil.

Aside from our domestic anxieties over water (we may, at last, have to build a tank or drill a well), the downside of future "glorious" summers has already been spelled out in Ireland's climate change scenarios.

Friends back from climbing Mweelrea Mountain were ecstatic at the ease of their march across slopes of crunchy, dried-up bog.

On the higher slopes, runs of hot, dry days shrink the peat and open cracks to the bedrock.

The very extremes of climate promised for parts of Ireland – both drought and deluge, in place of moderately cool summers and soft days, threaten large areas of blanket bog on the western hills.

The report on multiple landslides in north Mayo in September 2003 – more than forty of them, in spectacular falls – described the "cracked zones within the peat" that let an intense localised cloudburst sweep the steep bog from its moorings.

Invertebrate wildlife, meanwhile, wrestles with a parched terrain.

We may have been spared a few million midges whose eggs and larvae have dried out on the bogs. Many flies need the moister forms of rot and decay on which to feed, and ants and other insects need water to swell their eggs.

Dormancy and diapause are insect ways of waiting out a drought.

In the sand dunes, marram grass has rolled its leaves into tubes to reduce its water loss through transpiration. Little snails have climbed up the stems, where it is cooler, and closed their doors in the temporary opting-out known as summer aestivation.

Earthworms have retired to the bottom of their tunnels and slugs to their coolest, darkest corners underneath things.

Where are the migrant butterflies? Last summer saw a spectacular invasion of painted lady butterflies from Africa. This season's merest scatter of single painted ladies and red admirals speaks of strange weather in southern Europe. One looks at its weeks of downpours for an answer – weather, no doubt, that was really meant for us.

July 17th 2010
The heather blazing

The western hills had to wait for rain before blackened slopes, from Donegal to Connemara to Kerry, began to turn green again after an unprecedented, reckless scorching of the earth. Coillte alone counted 350 fires this spring, costing many millions in burnt conifer plantations.

The cost to nature was only to be guessed at in calcined hares, lizards and frogs, and charred or starved nestlings of hen harriers, stonechats, wrens, thrushes, pipits and larks.

The fires went on for many weeks past the legal cut-off date of 1 March. How many were purposeful, how many the madness of young vandals after the pub, we shall never know. Environmental groups have blamed a change in the single payment scheme that ties payment to farmers to "utilisable areas" of land. Scrubby hectares dotted with gorse don't qualify, and fire may have seemed the way to start reclaiming them.

There are laws that limit "traditional" burning, but gardaí find them unenforceable. ("Me, sergeant? Sure, I was up there trying to put it out!") Fire brigades, never so hard-pressed as this year, worry only about harm to people and property.

Given the scenarios of global warming, the future of the peaty western uplands is gloomy enough, as bog vegetation changes and high slopes of blanket peat dry out, crack open and slip off the rock. In my own landscape, a great landslide on the mountain across Killary Harbour from Leenane refuses to green over. In the heart of Connacht's sheep country, the scar evokes the last wave of human folly – decades of subsidised overgrazing of fragile peatland slopes.

Remedial farm plans have taken some effect, but most of the heather has vanished for good, and with it many of the botanically famous rarities of Ireland's mountain plant life. Some typical damage was spelled out this spring in the UK science journal Field Bryology, under the heartfelt heading "The tragedy of the Twelve Bens of Connemara: is there a future for Adelanthus lindenbergianus?" As little plants most people don't know exist, the liverworts tend to get stuck with only scientific names, "Lindenberg's featherwort" is at least a little easier to say, but what is so special about it? Like the mosses, liverworts were some of the earliest land plants of the planet, branching off the vegetable evolutionary tree below the ferns and then the plants with flowers.

Many of them seek out the shade of heather and other dwarf shrubs among the rocky scree of rain-soaked oceanic mountains. There they form a mat, often a striking mix of colours, that helps weld the stones together.

Lindenberg's featherwort is one of the larger liverworts, raising tufts of tiny overlapping leaves up to 10 centimetres high. It was first described by a German botanist in South Africa and grows also in tropical Africa and South and North America. But in Europe it has been found only on mountains in Donegal, Mayo, Galway and Kerry and on the western Scottish island of Islay. How it got to Europe (probably wind-borne spores) has been a mystery fascinating modern botanists, among them David Long of Edinburgh's Royal Botanic Gardens. Family links to Cleggan, in Connemara, have brought him to the Twelve Bens since the 1980s.

When the featherwort was first found there, in 1961, it grew abundantly with other liverworts on steep slopes some 550 metres high and covered with ankle-deep heather. Dr Long, too, found it easily in 1984. In 1994, at the peak of overgrazing, a botany group found "devastation – a few broken fragments of heather [and] small and sorry pieces of A. lindenbergianus." Since then, Dr Long has searched the Bens repeatedly without success, but in 2007 he found and photographed a small clump in steep, rocky terrain: "This could be," he writes, "literally the last survivor in the Bens." Another UK bryophyte specialist, David Holyoak, believes it is already too late for the liverwort heath to recover, "unless destocking were to be followed by reintroductions". Dr Holyoak has been working with Neil Lockhart, the bryophyte specialist at the National Parks and Wildlife Service, on a Red Data list of Ireland's endangered species.

When the overgrazing was at last acknowledged, all the western mountain commonages were mapped for damage and the numbers of sheep they could bear. (Unfortunately, as David Long observes, Connemara's sheep like to graze on the highest slopes.)

Conservation now depends on the farm plan scheme that has followed the rural environment protection scheme – this, of course, as long as the money holds up. In some visionary future, as botanists would wish, Connemara National Park may need to cover the Twelve Bens as a whole. In the meantime this summer's high walkers may care to watch where they're treading.

July 24th 2010

Our trees, all grown up

The tree surgeon proved not only to be skilled, devoted and a man of visual taste but to be a diplomat as well. "You did need some evergreens there," he supposed, "to break the wind in winter." This made us feel a bit less embarrassed about wanting the usual few metres off a clump of Lawson's cypress, so familiar to his profession as the towering folly of hedges in suburbia.

The fistful of left-over Lawson seedlings came with us from Dublin, along with the garden shed and bags of unused cow manure (this on a lorry with much else – planks, barrels and so forth – that "might come in useful" for the new life).

The little trees were planted hastily in odd corners of the acre, an open field only lately cleared of thistles and briars.

I doubt if I looked up while digging the holes. Or if I did, it was to discount any future in which little half-metre seedlings might reach a proper height. The ESB and phone lines, branching to our gable, webbed across a hillside in which hawthorn hedges and farm sycamores were shorn into stumpy wedges by the wind. Even the lopsided spruce at our gate had taken the best part of a century to rear its feathery flagpole.

We did not, indeed, set out to make a wood. But we reckoned without arboreal togetherness, egged on by recent decades of calmer, warmer springs.

The first windbreaks of timber slabs were subsumed into a maze of fuchsia hedges surrounding the vegetable beds and these, in turn, merged with the trees they protected, rearing up into spindly weavings of their own.

When the ocean winds blow now, they sift through Sitka, larch, birch and alder, ash and sycamore, rowan and willow, beech, oak, poplar – about a score of species, each with its own shape and nature. All have been planted – found room for, rather – as they came along. (If you love trees, they keep happening.)

In what was once the hen run, they have coalesced into a pool of cool, deep shade. The house, on a rise, has kept its outlook to the sea, and its bower of summer leaves dissolves in winter to give us back the mountain and traps the rising moon in bare branches.

From a distance we are, indeed, the old couple in the wood.

Worries about height and wires came only lately, and most acutely this spring, with (as the tree surgeon readily agreed) the greatest uprush of new growth in many years. The Lawson's cypress might never have reached the fifty metres they achieve in their native American forests, but their tips were already brushing the ESB power line.

Nearer the house, where the birds perch, a young ash was rapidly aspiring to follow suit. The phone line had already vanished between willow and oak, and the birch across the stream.

In a day's work with harness and saws, Ambrose Gaughan of Foxford restored our peace of mind, carving a new view to the hilltop and leaving a neat pile of logs in the shed. The cypresses now buttress the hawthorn hedge, and the ash is a still a graceful umbrella that will never spike the sky.

We have not had to touch our treasured memorial trees. There is Sally's lime, for the eccentric ladyship who gatecrashed our wedding and thus our lives, and David's ash for the farmer friend who should have been a forester.

The oak that John Healy reared from an acorn picked up beside the European Parliament in Strasbourg has just tipped its twigs with leaves of a rich and mysterious red. This is "lammas growth", the secondary spurt of leaves that makes up for the foliage that caterpillars eat. The red is extra tannin, to put them off.

John's friend was Douglas Gageby, this newspaper's great dendrophile editor, who, early on, sent me a cigar box of sprouting acorns wrapped in moss. His oaks adjoin the house, waiting on their own, more native, lammas growth. (For Scotland's lammas, read Lughnasa.)

But, yes, we did have to top one memorial tree, its past now mingled with our own. The old ragged spruce at the gate would not stop growing, even after seventy or eighty years of storms from the sea. It still bowed in the wind like a tall schooner's mast, but if it went – when it went – it would crash straight across the road.

It was the sole tree planted in the old life of half our house, a little Land Commission cottage built of fieldstone when the hill was striped almost a century ago.

Two-thirds of the spruce now remains, shorn of its dead branches, pruned to grow new foliage, and never again to lean in a force ten. But like the old bedroom door, still carved beneath the paint with children's names, it kept a claim on the life of a little piece of a hill.

July 31ˢᵗ 2010
A gift of mushrooms

The warmth of Connacht's long, dry spring was stored with particular benefit in the sandy undulations of the machair, the west's distinctive habitats of lawn-like turf behind the seashore, dusted by winter gales with limy seashell fragments and brightly carpeted just now with patches of purple wild thyme.

A neighbour who went fishing for mackerel on the headland came upon hundreds of field mushrooms in snowy arcs and circles on the turf. "It was strange," he reported, "seeing mushrooms growing literally feet from the ocean." Summer visitors brought us a big bag of them, gathered on the flat machair behind the dunes.

All this sent me out at dawn last week with dog and knapsack. It is most of twenty years since we had a really good mushroom summer – 1992 in the archives, with our first feast on 10 July. Weeks of sun, I noted then, had been followed by "days of silky drizzle from the sea" – conditions traditionally favourable for summoning the fruits of Agaricus campestris. This time it took a repeated, but very welcome, hammering of showers on the salty lawn of the duach.

Rather like the flowering of some kinds of orchid, predicting when and why mushrooms choose to fruit remains quite mysterious: mycologists still juggle with the interplay of temperature, moisture and nutrient supply. The "fairy rings", at least, are readily explained, as the fungus's underground network of mycelia, exhausting the soil's nutrients year by year, spreads out slowly to find more food. At the network's leading edge, the breakdown of organic food releases nitrogen, enough for the filaments' own sustenance, but also nourishing an extra growth of grass – hence the vivid ring of green in which the fungal fruits appear to shed their reproductive spores.

One circle that served our breakfast was about ten metres across, nourished over time by the droppings of sheep and rabbits. One might think these to be fairly evenly scattered, but their distribution is complicated by the advance of high spring tides. The water swirling in behind the dunes lifts the raisin-like droppings and gathers them at a dense and wavy tideline on the grass around the fairy rings.

August 14th 2010
Why badgers are bad news for wasps

The wasps come home to their nest a few at a time, converging like unsteady helicopters in an airspace at the corner of my eye. On this side of the glass, I'm trying to watch the evening Proms on telly; beyond it, the entry procession at the crack in the eaves is too wavering and out of tempo even for the slower bits of Shostakovich.

I could, of course, move my chair. And it's a small enough complaint to offer about life with Vespula vulgaris, our common social wasp. I dodge around the solitary queens in early spring, out from hibernation. Sometimes I find one rasping at the weathered grey wood of the shed door and mixing the fibres with spit for the paper to start her nest.

Later, as the queens' progeny grow into workers, the blossom of the cotoneaster tree is thronged exclusively by wasps, their short tongues tailored to the tiny, shallow flowers. This nectared energy is spent on catching and chopping up other garden insects, many of them not the gardener's friends. And it's only in late summer, for reasons I'll come to, that the wasps head for windfall apples in the orchard and other people's jam butties at the car park behind the strand.

There must, by now, be a whole line of nests in the roof space, for each queen starts a new one every year. She does all the early work, suspending a wood-pulp umbrella from the roof of a hole or a beam, moulding a tier of paper cells beneath it, then laying an egg in each. She has to feed the grubs with chewed-up caterpillars and other insects, and it's five weeks or so before the first brood grow into workers and take over the nest-building and foraging, feeding the grubs with macerated insects and leaving the queen to lay eggs. As the colony grows, each new tier of cells – a comb – is hung beneath the previous one by stalk-like pillars, producing an edifice rather like Dublin's Central Bank of Ireland building, only ball-shaped. It hangs within the spherical envelope of paper, leaving space so that air – and wasps – can circulate, entering and leaving through an opening at the bottom.

This is all very well for wasps in house roofs and sheds, but most queens begin with a mousehole or other small cavity in the ground.

How does the colony contrive a paper lantern almost the size of a football and containing eight or more tiers of comb? The answer is logical but awesome: the wasps enlarge the hole. They swallow water from a puddle, carry it back to the cavity, spit it out on the wall of the hole, scrape the mud off in pellets and then fly out to drop them, sometimes several metres away.

They may even push small stones out of the hole. What happens when they meet a big stone, as they certainly would in my garden, I have not learned.

As to the sweet tooth of wasps in late summer…Wasps, like ourselves, need carbohydrates for energy. As the workers feed the growing larvae with chewed-up insects, the grubs absorb the protein but dribble out the sugars in saliva, eagerly lapped up by their providers. In late summer, when broods are reared, this supply of carbohydrates dries up and has to be found elsewhere, in fruit or sticky drinks.

One natural sticky drink is the "honeydew" exuded at the anuses of aphids, the sap-sucking scale insects infesting plants and trees.

This surplus of sugary goo, dripping on to leaves and twigs, provides a medium for growth of the black mould that often disfigures garden plants beneath trees such as willows and limes. But it also meets the needs of myriad wasps, often in company with butterflies and ants. In New Zealand, indeed, where Vespula vulgaris is an undesirable alien, honeydew from aphids draws wasps in dense numbers to the sap-rich native beech forest, monopolising this sugar supply at the expense of indigenous insects and birds.

A bitter winter and wet summer have both worked this year to reduce Irish populations of flying insects, wasps among them. But what are their living controls? As a letter in today's Eye on Nature suggests, dragonflies are among the few predatory insects prepared to risk an attack.

But badgers will dig out the ground nests of wasps to feed on grubs and adults, ignoring the stings and scattering earth far and wide. On expert witness from the late Ernest Neal, "badgers account for a great number" of nests. People living in the Irish cattle counties officially cleared of badgers in the cause of reducing bovine TB will thus know who to blame for the buzzing in the kitchen.

October 2ⁿᵈ 2010
The joy of wood

The first whiff of woodsmoke from our chimney settles me comfortably into my skin: summer was never my season. And my love affair with wood goes all the way from growing trees and hugging them in a metaphorical way (the real thing isn't bad, either – a stirring embrace of toughness, mass and weight) to savouring their sacrifice on the hearth.

In between, of course, the lorryload of thinnings from the forest has to be reduced to stove-size logs, but even that can feel good. As summer waned, a run of sunny mornings took me over the wall to tackle the last, neglected layer of spruce trunks, each with ambitions to be, let's say, one-third of a telegraph pole.

The immediate object was to raise them into criss-cross rafts, open to every drying wind. Thinnings fresh from the forest are massively heavy and need a year to lose much of the water they've been pumping up to the crown. These were well aged but still untossable in the Scottish manner: rather to be slid over others, as on rollers, then lifted gingerly at one end, and eased up into the sun. Leverage (of the old-fashioned, non-banking kind) also came into its own.

In between heaves, there were rests on a rock amid the curling bracken, to take in the peace of the hillside, the plain and cheerful blueness of the sea. A robin whizzed in to seize the beetles I'd disturbed. And hovering in my mind was the truism that wood is the most wonderful substance and that doing almost anything with it – even hauling it about in one's old age – is no small enjoyment.

My family, it seems, have known this for many generations. Starting somewhere among Huguenot refugees to England, the first cabinet-making Viney worked in Devon in the eighteenth century. The woodworking line continued, well dowelled and dovetailed, to my father's apprenticeship to a Hampshire village carpenter at the age of twelve.

That my own skills have not ventured greatly beyond basic DIY is not the point, nor that the wood-carving chisels I brought from Dublin have never, after all, been used to high purpose: I just love the way wood looks and smells and feels, even when hewing it into logs with an electric chainsaw.

October 16th 2010
Spider in the loo

At leisure in the loo, a rather damp and chilly annex adapted from the old cottage porch, I take a generally benevolent inventory of the resident wildlife: small spiders in their webs around the window, woodlice patrolling the panelling, the odd baby slug grazing algae round the sink – even the occasional dearg a dhaol stalking woodlice in the shower.

Occasional pounces with a wisp of tissue keep the population under control, unless it's a big Tegenaria, whereupon removal may be delegated. There are people to whom this large house spider, so attentively poised, is almost a domestic pet. In its presence, however, I am seized with steely calm, prior to robotic action – or retreat. Even the echo of its form in the curly darkness of a tomato calyx, discarded on the kitchen bench, can prompt unease.

Most such phobias, seemingly, are fixed in children by the age of ten, often in response to the protective alarm of women. At nine, a bit pallid, and temporarily billeted in an open-air school in the healthy hills of Surrey, I was caught up in an early-morning flurry of nuns, who, discovering an outsize Tegenaria in a gleaming white washbasin of our cloakroom, swished back and forth in an agitated rustle of serge. They even brought whisky to pour on the animal, with what effect I do not remember – but such recollection seems highly suggestive.

Familiarity can help. Years ago, we had a cricket in the wardrobe, betrayed by its chirruping at bedtime. (The male can sing for hours.) Never having seen one, and consulting pictures, I found its tensed-up, grasshoppery regard a shade too alien for comfort. Ethna, however, started life in rural Cavan, where a cricket hidden somewhere in the hearth (and eating crumbs) was part of the luck in a house: she worried only that it might chew my socks.

October 23rd 2010
The other carbon dioxide problem

October's big spring tide coincided with days of very high pressure, so that the memorable calm of the hillside was echoed in the rise of the sea. It brimmed out of the channel more like slow mercury than water, creeping over sand and grass in a gradual, silent glaze. On the outer strand it rose to the lowest hummocks of the dunes and fell smoothly back, hemming the sand with lacy lines stitched by the smallest of bubbles.

The boreen to the sea was fringed by finches and linnets, dancing ahead of me and away over sandy pastures and cotton-wool sheep gilded by the sun. With no rumble of surf, the whirr of their wings was the day's loudest sound. At the channel the tide was still ebbing, to be waded in bare feet and trousers rolled up above the knee. It's ages since I did this, toes reaching for the softer, sandy bits, my balance not quite as sure as it used to be.

I have met baby flounders here, and sticklebacks, but the swift, glassy flow had sent them to shelter in cowlicks of green weed.

The water was thrillingly cold and then not cold at all.

The strand was ribbed in the flood's withdrawal and scattered with dark furls of Laminaria seaweed. The sand around them was pitted by the shore birds probing after burrowing sandhoppers. Otherwise, only random blobs, sheets and shards of plastic flotsam drew the eye.

I have gathered many useful plastic things: fish boxes and bottle crates, buoys and bits of net, tangles of cord – all grist to the landlubbing gardener. I have enough now, quite enough. And all, anyway, are the sweepings of storms, of which we've had few in a long time.

The sea has returned a great mass of sand, clothing the ribs of black rock. The cliffs it had carved in the dunes have had time to slide to a stable slope and grow a new haze of marram.

Other delicate tides have brought me whole window sills of collectibles – sea beans and sea urchin globes, the fragile violet sea snail, and more – none on this day. But the sand at the foot of the dunes was swagged with fresh drifts of seashells: limpet, mussel, razor, cockle, venus, carpet, trough, otter, wedge, tellin and the rest, a jumble of shapes, colours and fragments of small ocean lives.

The substance of them all is calcium – or, rather, the kind of calcium carbonate known as aragonite, named for an eccentric twinning of its crystals in rocky veins of that part of Spain that produced a famous Catherine. (I've started, so I'll finish.) Aragonite also gives pearls their sheen, and abalone shells their rainbow iridescence.

More essentially, it builds the shells and skeletons of billions of sea organisms, from deep-sea corals to the bivalves of the Irish shore. For others the main building block is calcite, a tougher, less soluble form of carbonate.

The ocean is still alkaline, its upper layers saturated with carbonate ions. But the extra carbon dioxide absorbed into the sea from human industry has already swung its pH the other way, by almost a third. The acidification of the ocean is now "the other carbon dioxide problem", looming ever more urgently in scenarios of climate change.

Human-generated carbon has penetrated deeply into the north Atlantic, becoming more corrosive with greater cold and pressure, and in the long term the surface layer of shell-friendly water could get shallower and shallower. But already there are forecasts that, in the Arctic, aragonite could begin to diminish at the surface within a few decades.

What happens when marine animals are bathed in acidifying seawater? Research is still in its infancy and full of paradoxical results.

In some studies sea urchins and brittle stars have lost their body functions, oyster growth has dwindled, marine snails have started losing their shells. Other molluscs have damaged immune systems or have forgotten how to dodge their predators. Not every species reacts severely. Crabs, lobsters, starfish, barnacles and even limpets seem better able to cope with changes in pH, but even these are vulnerable in the early stages of life.

If dissolved aragonite disappears from the deep Atlantic, the slow-growing cold-water corals off Ireland seem likely to be among the first organisms to suffer.

The waters around Ireland have distinctive patterns of seasonal upwellings, raising deep water, lower in aragonite, to spill across the continental shelf. Our coastal topographies, currents and plankton fronts can all affect the pace and degree of acidification.

December 4th 2010
Surviving a harsh winter

Inside that little sphere of fluff clinging to the feeder is a body not much bigger than a ping-pong ball, its ratio of heat-leaking skin surface to volume of bird a distinctly dodgy fit for icy weather: in the Arctic you get not blue tits but big snowy owls with bulky anoraks and feathered galoshes. And inside the soft weave of down under a tit's fluffed-up feathers is a tiny heart going bang-bang-bang 500 times a minute to pump some of the warmest blood of any animal: forty degrees compared with our thirty-seven. All that need for energy, that racing metabolism, and still it has to fight for a place at the nuts.

There are probably many more blue tits around than there would be without garden feeders. And before peanuts and fancy seeds there were (at least where I grew up) doorstep milk bottles with tops of foil or cardboard.

The tits spread the word across Europe about the feed of cream inside – all of them had the knowledge within a couple of post-war years.

Even now, new hedgerow birds are learning about the winter largesse of back gardens: woodpeckers, siskins, above all the glorious goldfinches – a dozen of them now at our feeders in the oak trees, battling it out with the sparrows. There are still emails asking "What is this wonderful bird?" from readers at a first rapt encounter, and a visit by forty of them at a garden in Waterford must have seemed magical, indeed. A reader in Wicklow last month reported the success of a small feeder filled with nyjer, the tiny black oilseeds from Africa: within days, up to eighteen goldfinches were clinging there. "How," wondered Robert Myerscough, "did they recognise it in the first place, and how did they get the word out to their mates?"

As the temperature plummeted this week, one's ecological concerns were softened by ordinary, irrational sympathies. In the battles over oat flakes on our kitchen window sill we welcomed a pair of song thrushes, each with its own rich livery of speckles, and booed the anonymous blackbirds that drove them away. I have been out at first light to refill the box, hoping to give the thrushes a better chance.

Blackbirds are every bit the bullies they're painted, habitually robbing smaller birds of their food. David Snow, in a classic study of the species, thought them even more ruthless than mistle thrushes or fieldfares, both notoriously domineering. But at feeders it's the blackcap that seems most aggressive – a mere warbler that often seems able to chase everything else away.

As I write, a near-total absence of both fieldfares and redwings at this corner of the Connacht coast presents a disquieting mystery.

These Scandinavian thrushes are regular migrants to Ireland in late autumn and fly west for refuge ahead of extreme winter weather.

In one day last January the bird painter Michael O'Clery reported 20,000 redwings and 5,000-6,000 fieldfares arriving from the sea at Ballinskelligs, Co Kerry. A few days later, the clifftops at Courtmacsherry, Co Cork, were covered with hundreds of the birds "so tired", as Peter Wolstenholme wrote, "that we were able to pick up the featherweight waifs, which almost expired in our hands".

Thousands, indeed, did die, especially among the redwings, from Cork up to Mayo and beyond – among them, probably, the dozen I flushed unintentionally one morning from their roost at the heart of an escallonia bush.

Surviving bitter nights is the big challenge for songbirds, which makes their different habits all the more intriguing. Blue tits and great tits, for example, seek individual shelter in crevices and tree holes, tucking beaks and legs into their feathers. (When blue tits have paired early, the male sees his mate to bed, then goes to roost nearby.) The only slightly smaller long-tailed tits, on the other hand, flying in little flocks by day, clump together in a ball at night, tails sticking out, at the heart of a hawthorn bush.

Wrens may hold the record for snuggling down together: fifty in one nest box seems to be the current record. Last February a reader in Co Antrim emailed a photograph of wrens packed into a swallow's nest in a corner of her porch. Once they're all in, no one uses the front door.

Insect-feeders such as wrens are not drawn to peanuts, but will occasionally take crumbs or suet from the ground, and a Greystones reader last winter reported a treecreeper eating peanut crumbs beneath his feeders. Starlings, too, were coming to feeders for the first time in Co Tipperary, and rooks in Co Wicklow waiting patiently beneath them, for nut crumbs.

A pied wagtail joining our window sill thrushes is different, but scarcely rare, and certainly no match for the snipe in people's gardens last February, jabbing desperately into rose beds in the search for soil invertebrates.

December 11ᵗʰ 2010

Crying for the curlew

With the sea asleep and the wind behind the ridge, the silence of an icy morning can reach all the way to the horizon. I listen for anything: the whooping chorus of swans on David's lake or sheep shuffling through the rushes across in Connemara. If I cough, there'll be a bark from Ross, the farm collie down the hill.

One sound I've been listening hard for has always summoned up the west in just a couple of plaintive notes: cour-lee.

It reminds me of an inspired television commercial there was in the 1980s. It featured an expatriate engineer somewhere in the Middle East, sweating in a hard hat, and longing for Sally O'Brien and the way she might look at you, along with a glass of Harp and the curlew's cry.

Now it seems the native curlew, Ireland's iconic wader, is in danger of leaving home. Even the onset of another Arctic winter hasn't conjured great numbers of them from Scotland and elsewhere in Europe.

BirdWatch Ireland reckons that well over eighty per cent of the Irish breeding population has been lost since the 1970s, falling from some 12,000 pairs to just a few hundred. Last summer Stormont took the bird off the hunters' quarry list in Northern Ireland. Curlews in the Republic may still be shot this winter – an absurdity pointed up, in passing, in a Senate debate last month.

In practice, few self-respecting Irish shooters have aimed at a curlew in years, and Ireland's open season is now shared only with France. A management plan for Europe's curlew produced for the European Commission in 2007 blamed the widespread decline not on hunting (though the shooting in France "may have consequences for those segments of population that pass through") but mainly on loss of breeding habitat and the loss of chicks to predators.

This is echoed by BirdWatch Ireland, which cites moorland vanishing under conifers, the bogs cut over, and marginal hill land drained and ploughed, or abandoned and covered with rushes and scrub.

Such wholesale loss of suitable upland habitat seems unlikely on the face of it. But, in the lowlands, drainage and intensive management of grassland have taken their toll on the bird's nesting ground.

Even in the moist, unploughed native grasses of the Shannon Callows, the curlew joins other native waders – lapwing, redshank and snipe – in severe decline. Their nests are swamped by mounting summer floods, and spreading scrub favours their predators.

Ground-nesting waders want open nesting habitats with clear views, and the nearest tree at least 100 metres away. In agreement with farmers, Bird-Watch Ireland has been clearing scrub and using trial anti-predator fences at nesting time.

The Cry of the Curlew is BirdWatch's current appeal for €99,000 for a programme to check the bird's national losses. It will use this to find out where the last few hundred are breeding and then to improve or protect their habitats by clearing gorse and other scrub, blocking ditches to re-wet upland pastures, or looking for changes in grassland management. In Northern Ireland special action focuses on restoring wet grassland around Lough Neagh, a key area for curlew nesting.

Just now, of course, any chevron of curlews that flies my way, gliding down to the shore on arched wings, is most likely to have started out far to the east.

And while last week I was puzzling over the lack of migrant redwing and fieldfares on my hillside, the resurgence of the winter chill seems certain to bring great flocks of refugees.

At Ireland's coasts the peregrine falcons are already poised to kill their share.

Among my window sill bric-a-brac is the perfect skull and bill of a curlew, a delicate ivory sculpture picked up on an island off the mouth of Killary Harbour. The skull is no bigger than a pigeon's egg, but the bill, with its flawless, fragile curve, is 13 centimetres long. The tip is full of tiny perforations made to carry nerves that give the curlew its exquisite sense of touch.

When I found it years ago I wondered what had happened to the rest of the bird. Then I happened to read RM Lockley's classic Letters from Skokholm (the title of which refers to an island off Pembrokeshire), in which one of his picnics was interrupted by a wild shriek from the sky: "Looking up, we were in time to see a peregrine strike a curlew at about one hundred feet above us. The curlew's head was struck off close to the base of the skull, and fell beside us. The body fell into the sea, from which the peregrine made no attempt to retrieve it, but on seeing us flew away."

February 19th 2011

A shrew in the loo

What do you do with a shrew in the loo? This lunatic, unquenchable jingle was born of the latest addition to the biodiversity of what was once our cottage porch. Veteran readers will already be familiar with my meditations on its wildlife – woodlice, spiders, the dearg a dhaoil in the shower, and so on – so the shift up the food chain should come as no surprise.

The pygmy shrew is an arch-insectivore (like the hedgehog) and nothing to do with the mouse family, so that its rapid skittering around my bedroom slippers impelled only the lifting of feet lest some entomological morsel escape that quivering little snout and grinding, ruby-tipped teeth. Two hours without a meal and a shrew is in a bad way ("There is something indescribably sad, almost poignant, about a dead shrew," wrote the Belfast zoologist James Fairley once, "flat on its back with its little legs in the air. As animal corpses go, only that of an elephant is more pathetic."

As the smallest mammal we have, Sorex minutus actually shrinks further in winter – often to less than three grams, around the weight of a two-cent coin – and the negligible skeleton inside that little ball of dark, velvety fur permits an easy wriggle into the warmth of many rural houses. Ours is perhaps more permeable than most, so what one actually does about a shrew in the loo is let it come and go (meanwhile alerting one's spouse; not that mine is much given to shrieks).

March 26th 2011

When hares turn white

It took a couple of days with loppers, bush saw and shredder to reduce the rampant escallonia bush outside my workroom window to something like an ordinary hedge. At my computer next morning I revelled in the long-lost view: a glowing Inishturk stretched out on the horizon, a small, neat inshore trawler unzipping a calm sea, right to left. But magically more, the rushy pasture beyond the hedge presented my first winter-white Irish hares.

The body of one was almost wholly white, with a dusting of silver-grey hairs on its back. Its face and the fronts of its ears were, however, the normal dark brown, as dramatic as a Halloween mask. Then appeared two more hares, their underparts also brilliantly white. In the mad March chasing and circling that ensued the whitest hare was my favourite to start boxing for a woman's right to choose.

An icy winter must have produced more than the usual share of whitened Irish hares.

Most books insist that they rarely undergo a winter colour change, unlike the Scottish or Scandinavian mountain hares. But the rarity may be just that of extremely icy winters.

Recent weeks have brought several reports of white hares to Eye on Nature, all from the west. In Northern Ireland a conservation group called Irish Hare Initiative has mounted a white hare survey. A map on its website shows almost 100 sightings spread across the island, clustered most densely in the midlands west of Dublin.

Occasional white Irish hares have been reported for well over a century. In the late 1800s the eminent but ageing naturalist Alexander More noticed, while being pushed in his bath chair through the streets of Dublin, "that after only a week of snowy weather about the middle of January, the number of hares hung up in the poulterers' shops showing these light patches become conspicuously greater than they had been at the beginning of the month". Today, as the mammalogist James Fairley sums up, "In a given area it sometimes happens that some will turn almost completely white, others will be half-and-half and still others may only whiten a little or not at all." Lepus timidus hibernicus is a race of the Arctic hare. On an expedition to northeast Greenland, to help David Cabot ring barnacle geese, I was charmed by the scores of fluffy, snow-white animals, surreally nibbling at yellow poppy flowers in the midnight sun.

They could not have been more conspicuous on stony hillsides thawed out for the summer, their leverets an easy target for any passing raven or gyrfalcon. But, in the numbers game of natural selection, the year-round whiteness of High Arctic hares has to benefit the population as a whole.

As much as for camouflage in snow, the whiteness of northern animals and birds seems to relate to temperature: the farther north, the whiter they tend to be. Like the cells of the polar bear's white fur, or those of the feathers of the snowy owl, those of the white hare are filled with air, an insulation that reduces heat loss from the body.

The winter whitening of mountain hares in Scotland and other northern countries is achieved by a third moult of the year, beginning in October and perhaps partly triggered by the shortening length of day.

Fine but dense hairs, empty of the usual melanin pigment, are projected to take the place of the brown ones, producing an often strikingly sudden change of colour. In Ireland it has been generally supposed that there are only two moults, so that genetic control of pigmentation remains something of a mystery. Some observers have reported hares with white patches outside the winter season.

Our subspecies of Arctic or mountain hare is not called hibernicus for nothing. Indeed, research by the Quercus conservation unit at Queen's University Belfast has suggested enough genetic divergence from Scottish or other races to warrant the animal's promotion to a full species.

As a survivor of Ireland's last ice age, it may even link, uniquely, to a former species of mountain hare once common in Europe.

Today its most obvious distinction is its island-wide distribution, right down to the edge of the sea, together with the widely remarked "rarity" of whitening in winter.

Exceptionally low temperatures in the last two winters or the extent of snow on the ground may have triggered a third, much later moult in many Irish hares. In his last book on Ireland's furry animals, A Basket of Weasels (2001), James Fairley found that this possibility "apparently has never been explored". A systematic study of winter whitening was, he thought, "long overdue".

April 2nd 2011

In praise of toads

"What has biodiversity ever done for me?"The question chimed rhetorically at the end of a letter to this newspaper last Monday about the cost of saving Ireland's last migrant corncrakes. The writer implied that money paid to farmers to avoid mowing down corncrakes nesting in their silage meadows would be better spent on a few more metres of motorway.

The next day a political correspondent of another newspaper was making mischief on the subject of counting natterjack toads. The Department of the Environment has just commissioned consultant ecologists to spend two years studying the breeding success of the toads – one of Ireland's more vulnerable species – to fulfil commitments under the EU habitats directive.

Not so long ago, ran the story, Taoiseach Enda Kenny was mocking John Gormley for spending money on a study of the Irish frog population (again at the EU's behest, as frogs are in trouble across much of the world). "Are we," asked Kenny then, "to see the spectre of the Minister, Deputy Gormley, in his sandals, tramping through the wetlands of the midlands counting frogs at dawn or dusk?" Such provocations coincide with the publication of the first big inventory of Irish wildlife, great and small, by the National Biodiversity Data Centre. This agency, in Waterford, was set up on the initiative of the Heritage Council as a basic tool of research and policy for nature conservation and land use. Funded by the Department of the Environment, it has gathered some 1.6 million records of Ireland's species, from algae to eagles. They now number more than 31,000, with at least another 10,000 (at a wild guess) to be found on and around the island.

All very worthy, as the letter writer might agree, but what has biodiversity ever done for me? I have long disliked the lofty otherness of this academic coinage, compressing "biological diversity". It quite lacks the warmth and engagement of "nature" or "wildlife". But it does have real meaning, if one that, more and more, must be spelled out in the cash value of nature's "ecosystem services".

Thus, at the launch of this month's biodiversity inventory, the centre's director, Dr Liam Lysaght, priced the insect pollination of human food plants at an estimated €85 million a year and part of a national benefit he put at €2.6 billion. The new Minister for Heritage, Jimmy Deenihan, spoke of the island's diversity of species as "cultural capital" for the attraction of ecotourism. "We have something very special," he added hopefully.

Ireland's natterjack toads may have been a bit too special for their own good. Their arrival and survival at the head of Dingle Bay, in Kerry, at the end of the Ice Age is part of a challenging saga of dispersal still being unravelled by geneticists. With a central abundance in Portugal and Spain, their populations now extend through seventeen countries, ranging from northern England to Poland and Belarus.

So there are of pockets of them across Europe as a whole, just as corncrakes are still holding their own on unintensified farmland in eastern Europe. But this protected Irish species has a conservation status that is officially bad – this pending a study of whether ninety new ponds for breeding could slowly bring their numbers back.

Natterjacks need to breed in warm, shallow ponds free of vegetation and of predators that eat their tadpoles – ideally, transient ponds that dry up at the right time in summer. The toads once spawned right around the shores of Castlemaine Harbour, on Dingle Bay, but as coastal farmland was drained, numbers fell by perhaps half. With the toads' traditional ponds down to about a dozen, the National Parks and Wildlife Service set out to create a lot more, helped with some funding from the Heritage Council.

Ponds created previously at Castlegregory golf links had already shown great success. In 2008 and 2009, forty-five farmers around Castlemaine and near Fermoyle (the toads' other traditional station), also on Tralee Bay, dug two ponds each in their coastal pastures – shallow saucers about fifteen metres across and no more than a metre deep. An annual €500 per pond for five years also rewards them for keeping them clear of reeds by hand and controlling grazing to keep the grass short.

The right kind of rain in spring can produce huge numbers of yellow-striped toadlets, a mere centimetre long when they first venture on to land. A dry year, on the other hand, can lead to mass mortality. It may take many years for numbers to build in enough of the ninety new ponds. As a positive augury, the first males began calling at Fermoyle in mid-March, a full month ahead of schedule.

As it happens, both natterjack and corncrake have penetrating, far-carrying calls, each quite exceptional of their kind. Both can make a quiet night magical – which is all, I suppose, they ever did for us.

April 9th 2011

The science of sheep

The sheep on the lawn at daybreak tested my goodwill with a few more illicit mouthfuls, then lolloped away into the shadows. I followed at a gentle distance, down into the trees and through a mangrove tangle of ancient fuchsia branches.

A tuft of wool on barbed wire finally betrayed the point of trespass: a wind-toppled bush had flattened the fence just enough for the sheep, poised on the grassy hedge bank, to pick her way forward.

Bush saw and binder twine enabled a lash-up for yet another time being.

Such episodes are no surprise on the hungry eve of lambing (or "yeaning", as my neighbours prefer). What interested me about this one was that, by all behavioural accounts, sheep avoid shadows and always move towards the light. But this animal had crossed from a sunny bank into deep tree shadows, without a blade of grass in sight, to reach, at some dark distance, a lawn it could never have seen (but perhaps could smell on the breeze).

The puzzle pales when set against recent discoveries about the mental capacities of sheep. So often thought stupid, subject to unreasonable mass terrors and quite incapable of deciding which way to run off the road, they turn out to be discriminating individuals, with substantial memories and capacity for conscious thought and emotion.

Much of this has probably been intuited by farmers for generations, but the science can still impress.

Dr Keith Kendrick is head of the laboratory of cognitive and behavioural neuroscience at the Babraham Institute, in Cambridge, England. He has been leading experiments on sheep for decades, studying the workings of the neural systems of their brains as they respond to what they see or smell, or to other chemical cues. This is not, necessarily, for the ultimate benefit of sheep (though some may have spun off in the process) but for closer understanding of mammalian responses in general.

Many of the conclusions rest on the ability of the sheep to remember old faces, whether of others in a flock or of humans. Set to gaze at pictures of faces and encouraged by food rewards, they learned to remember fifty other sheep faces, some for more than two years.

Even more significantly for neurobiology, they were using the same specialised neural cells, on the right side of the brain, as humans.

These also encoded not only the absent faces but also how the sheep felt about them.

And while those of dogs and humans usually carried "a common negative emotional significance", a familiar human face, on sufficient acquaintance, and doing friendly things like bringing food, earns being encoded with those of fellow sheep. Indeed, sheep shut stressfully into an isolation chamber can be calmed down by being shown pictures of sheep or people they know and feel good about: their hearts slow, they bleat less, their adrenaline falls.

Vets, farmers and zoo keepers could conceivably make use of all this. And, as Kendrick's team suggested in 2004, "One method of relieving separation anxiety in young children may also be to give them pictures of their parents to carry." The link between recognising faces and responding appropriately to their expressions seems often to break down in human afflictions such as autism and schizophrenia, so to find it working in the same neural systems in sheep and people guarantees their laboratory careers – scalp electrodes, heart monitors, postmortem brain analysis and all.

Sheep now rate with monkeys in the study of individual facial recognition and recollection, skills the animals clearly use as part of their normal lives. Their response to chemical signals has also been under research. Oxytocin, for example, the "love hormone" that figures in human birth and breastfeeding, also bonds the ewe with her lambs and compels her fierce denial of milk to the young of any other mother.

The past few decades have taught us a lot about the common sensibilities of mammals and other species. The intelligence of so many fellow creatures, from chimpanzees to crows, continues to amaze, and where memory and conscious thought exist, emotional capacity cannot be far away.

The sudden gleam of newborn lambs will brighten the hillside in coming weeks, and the bleating of lambs and their anxious mothers will rise at times to an irritating background chorus. Lambs can take a month, perhaps two, to recognise their mothers, and shrill bleats seek their location as they wander off to play.

Meanwhile, if the ewe should appear on the lawn again, I will put on my smiley Obama T-shirt and inquire, in the friendliest manner, how the devil she managed to get in this time.

One likes to be well remembered, even by a sheep.

April 16th 2011

Three weeks on Haughey's island

Michael Viney Inishvickillane '85

Such a shame that the one taoiseach to count love of nature among the finer things in life should have been such a villain in pursuing all the others. No one matched Charles Haughey in looking out for Ireland's nature and history. The idea of the Heritage Council, the State's sanctuary for whales and dolphins, the rescue of Coolattin Woods, in Co Wicklow, the Discovery archaeology programme, the Céide Fields go-ahead: all were among things to his credit.

In Government Buildings his special adviser on environmental affairs, Dr David Cabot, beavered away at Green 2000, a committee report full of nature-friendly ideas. Then this week it was reported that his family has offered his yacht Celtic Mist, which had been for sale for €175,000, to the Irish Whale and Dolphin Group, for its research work.

Much of Haughey's personal grá for nature was played out on the heights of Inishvickillane, in the Blaskets off Co Kerry.

He finally bought the island in the early 1970s, but the idea had taken root years earlier, before the turmoil of the arms trial and his fight back to leadership.

A voluminous archive of papers and photographs of Haughey's relationship with the island, donated by his family, is now on digitised display at the Blascaod Centre, in Dún Chaoin, west of Dingle. It holds two copies of The Wild Island, a series from The Irish Times in September 1965. This was my diary as a castaway, camped alone on Inishvickillane for three memorable weeks.

I was young – thirty-two – and it shows, rather, in some over-the-top prose and blushworthy confidences. ("The sun set red tonight and I watched it all the way down, smoking a last pipe and listening to the Beethoven violin concerto," or, "I crawled from the sleeping bag as from a chrysalis and stretched in the sun. Suddenly properly hungry for the first time in days, I hacked thick slices off the slab of bacon and played Vivaldi's "Le Printemps" while they sizzled…" I had eight hours of cassettes and twenty hours of batteries, so there's rather a lot of this.)

The island, however, had splendid sounds of its own, and a wildness even sharper since the last of the Ó Dálaigh family were taken off to the mainland, in the 1950s. Their sons still came out by currach from Dún Chaoin on a calm summer's day to shear a little flock of sheep, but without them Inishvickillane was often as described by Robin Flower, who went there once on a rabbit-catching expedition.

He felt it "inhabited with the sense of loneliness: it is as though it were at the last end of things, dwelling in a silence which the ceaseless murmur of the sea around its base and the whining gulls about its summit rather accentuate than disturb". But the ocean could do a lot more than murmur.

I pitched my tent first near the island's one surviving house, its tarred roof drooping and bound down with cables, a sundial outside the door. A summer storm on the sixth day drove me to stone walls for shelter. At its height, the rain penetrated the tent as a fine mist, and stays began snapping around me. Retrieving my gear from its collapse was, I wrote, "like swimming in a wet bed". Haughey, too, was to move the site of his holiday home (a modest enough cottage, if one discounts the helicoptered labour) into the lee of the island's ridge.

That also avoided disturbing the thousands of storm petrels, whose summer nesting in burrows and stone walls is the great natural treasure of the island. Their midnight return from the sea to feed their chicks found my tent in their way, so that the sudden, chirruping blizzard of wings became something out of Hitchcock, the invisible birds scrabbling and sliding down the fabric over my head.

Haughey's own wildlife experiments sought to improve on Eden – or at least to furnish it more fully. His attempt to restore sea eagles to the cliffs didn't work: just one pair, from Germany, was nowhere near enough, and the birds were ferociously mobbed by the islands' big gulls and ravens. Aillil, the male, was found dead on a beach in Waterville; Maeve came and went for a few years after but finally disappeared.

The nine red deer flown from Killarney were a better idea – indeed, a very good one, as the island's herd, now at about ninety, duly culled and renewed, preserve the bloodline, safe from interbreeding with the mainland's Sika deer.

I doubt if Charlie ever stewed a rabbit on a fire of dried sheep dung or had the grey seals snatching pollack off his spinner. But, with a glass of good claret in his hand, he must have known those incredible evenings when, as I wrote, "a theatrical clarity of light lent the islands new perspectives: deep avenues of cliffs like vistas in a Piranesi, gleaming and gold-enamelled (slow bursts of spun-glass spray)". He did invite me back, any time. But I left my wild island, and my youth, back in the mists.

May 14th 2011

Things that go korrk-kok! in the night

Every morning for weeks on end the spring medley of birdsong on the acre was shouted down by a rasping, penetrating squawk – korrk-kok! – married to a loud whirr of wing beats. At times last month this erupted every five or ten minutes, sometimes making me jump just the other side of the hedge.

The cock pheasant's advertising call can carry well over a kilometre, and a note of desperation (or so I fancied) began to creep into it. Then yesterday, hearing a different sound – a chuckling rather than a crowing – I glanced between the hawthorn to catch cock pursuing hen in low flight across the stone walls. The gun club hadn't let him down after all.

Once heard, the pheasant's proclamation is unmistakable, and it ceases by sundown. Some bird sounds at dusk and after can be powerfully mysterious. You tend to remember, for example, where you were at first encounter with the "drumming" of a snipe. (For me, one young, boozy night in the Dublin Mountains: "Bloody hell!" cried someone, in the awed silence afterwards.) Drumming is not a good word for the eerie, resonant huhuhuhuhuhuhuhu! of the snipe's forty-five-degree plunge above one's head, wings and outer tail feathers angled to tease vibrations from the air. "Heatherbleat" is one old name for the bird.

This summer, however, seems notable for another night sound, a cricket-like chirring, often at dusk, going on for ages like somebody's sewing machine. Its mystery is doubled by one's doubt about direction: just where in that shadowy thicket…? As Gilbert White described, it "seems to be close by, though at a hundred yards' distance, and when close at your ear is scarce any louder than when a great way off".

It's a summer regular to Ireland from west Africa, but birders have been reporting exceptional arrivals. Male grasshopper warblers, once tucked away and switched on, tend to stay put in one spot as they chirr, and, even when spotted, they will often carry on obligingly while you're moving in for a close-up.

Nightjars, with their own, distinctive variation on the theme, are far less accessible and, being masters of camouflage, manage to look quite un-bird-like even when singing from the top of a bushy tree.

The hypnotic advertising call of the male, rising and falling in the dusk, was once so widely known in Ireland that it earned the bird the name of túirne lín, or spinning wheel.

It loved "low, scrubby woods on hillsides", wrote Richard Ussher in the late 1800s, "and heaths bordering plantations. In such places several may be heard churring at the same time." Today perhaps fewer than thirty pairs arrive from southern Africa to breed. This is part of a general decline in western Europe, although some of Coillte's young, restocked conifer plantations may help provide new habitat.

The nightjar family is Caprimulgidae, a name that chimes in odd support of an old country name of "goatsucker". This sprang from a myth, as old as Aristotle and Pliny, that the wide gape of the nightjar's bill was admirably made for sucking milk from goats and cows. In fact, it's rather like the open maw of a basking shark and, fringed with whiskers, lets the bird hoover up midges and moths as it flies.

The presence of nightjars on YouTube is fitful, with recordings of distant song that have to be turned up to full volume, and sparse, spooky footage of the bird in flight in the Netherlands or in clearings of the New Forest in England.

There, as the "fern owl", it has been watched by Richard Mabey. When the song stops and the bird takes wing, he writes, "a branch seems to break free and float towards you, and suddenly the fern owl is glancing over the tops of the trees, narrow wings arched above its back and bouncing, as if it were being tugged like a kite up towards the night sky".

Which leaves, of course, the corncrake, well grounded in dense cover, Ireland's iconic chorister of nights in May and June. In hard times some have begrudged the cost of paying farmers to mow their meadows inside out, but 2010 did see the first rise in numbers in years.

These farmers' grants have now been taken in house by the National Parks and Wildlife Service, leaving BirdWatch Ireland to manage its own corncrake habitats, in Mayo and on Donegal islands, with funding from the Heritage Council.

Let's hope it lasts.

June 11ᵗʰ 2011

Gardening by the sea

It took a few days to show the full effect of gaoth ruadh, the blasting, red-
dening wind from the sea. The storm that banjaxed a presidential helicopter
swept through the summer gardens of the west, flaying potatoes in Donegal,
shredding lettuce in Achill, tossing magpies from their nests in Connemara.
And with the wind came an invisible flux of salt spray to scorch the seaward
flanks of trees and hedges into a dismal, autumnal withering.

On our acre, the polytunnel held firm in its new, tight skin, and the wind
roared up the tall hedges and over the canopy of trees.

Before we had such shelter, warnings of summer storms would send us
out with big pieces of fishing net salvaged from the shore: spread across the
potatoes and tied to stakes, they calmed the tender haulm and saved the
crop. Now even my tall broad beans, while laid low, have raised their flowering stems again.

The salt damage is dramatic and oddly precise, like the work of some
demon with a blowtorch. I look out at an elder tree divided into two, the
inward half still green and panicled with creamy blossom, the seaward half
hanging in dark shreds. A beech tree that had grown so bravely and beautifully domed has been seared into a wedge shape after all.

Wind-moulded trees are iconic of the west – flagged, as some foresters say: tilting arabesques of hawthorn, sloping farmhouse sycamores.

Neither is an actual bending to the wind, but a steady, chemical shearing of seaward shoots by aerosols of salt, leaving active growth to stream out from the leeward side of the tree. In a big winter storm, the flight of salt droplets whipped from the crests of waves can dowse the whole coastal margin in spray. (At the old Brackloon oakwood, beside Croagh Patrick, a cycle of January storms once delivered, in two weeks, seventy-eight per cent of the salt for the whole year.) At the first kilometre of coast, the droplets are actually seawater, with its load of the main marine ions: sodium chloride, magnesium and sulphate. As the wind travels inland, the droplets are smaller, but still carry salt that can be licked from one's skin.

This storm swept salt further inland than any in living memory, but the old men like to say that. There was a hurricane in New England that scorched trees as far as 70 kilometres inland, and chlorine from salt spray has recently been found high in the sky over the very middle of the United States. Air parcels that travel long distances over the sea are increasingly loaded with salt, so that rain falling at the coast can have several times the content of sodium as seawater itself.

Sodium in the soil stresses plants by limiting their water intake; drawn into the cells chloride ions can be toxic, the edges of leaves curling and crisping into death. Half a century ago, An Foras Talúntais (now Teagasc) looked at the resources of west Donegal and saw salt spray as one good reason for not trying to grow strawberries, for example (this in the days before polytunnels).

Even in July, Malin Head gets ten times as much sodium as Birr in Co Offaly.

May's salty storm was doubly unfortunate in that it hit the crops of people who were growing their own for the first time.

Others were returning to a lifestyle that included a regular self-sufficiency in potatoes, cabbage and carrots – food which, for a few years, had been happily ceded to the supermarket.

The wind also arrived at a littoral that was aglow with new and beautiful flower gardens.

They had suffered one shock already: the impact of unprecedented winter frosts on tender shrubs and hedges. The gale whipped around shrivelled cordylines, gaunt skeletons of griselinia, withered swords of New Zealand flax. The gardeners of the west and their attendant plant nurseries may need to grow wise in species to survive both salt and ice.

Many plants are indeed salt-tolerant, or halophyte, and in a world where freshwater is becoming a scarce resource and much farmland is turning saline, plants happy at the sea's edge could have a future as human food crops. Sea kale, for example, once plentiful on Ireland's coastal shingle banks, makes a delicious garden vegetable when its big spring shoots are blanched under buckets or clay pots. Trialled by a Dutch university, it responded to increasing salinity with even thicker and juicier leaves.

Wild sea beet is another halophyte, and it gave us the succulent stems of Swiss chard.

There could be lessons here about gardening by the sea.

June 18th 2011
Right-handed and left-handed animals

In the thirteenth year after her rescue from a dog orphanage, Meg, a cuddly cross of Labrador and spaniel, is living on borrowed time. A swim through the river to the big strand below us no longer prompts those wide and ecstatic circlings over the sand; instead, more and more often, there are hopeful pauses to suggest we might go home again.

When she did run, which way was it: clockwise or anticlockwise? My mind's eye says the former. A reader, John Elwes of Kilballyquilty, in Co Waterford, reports that his "very intelligent border collie" runs anticlockwise, prior to rounding up bullocks.

He suggests an exploration of the handedness of animals in general: how unique are people in using left or right? Debate on the significance of handedness in nature goes back centuries to philosophers like Leibniz and Kant. Even in this column, over the years, the handedness of snails and climbing beans has seemed fit for disquisition. Down in the dunes, the prettily banded Cepea nemoralis follows most snails in coiling to the right (except occasionally it doesn't). And, down in the polytunnel, all the climbing beans are coiling up their strings anticlockwise (unless you're looking up from the bottom, like a bean).

Back to the circling dogs, engaged in what science now calls "behavioural lateralisation".

One might conjecture about inheritance from wolves, reported as patrolling their hunting routes "always counterclockwise". But the abundant research into lateralisation now spans almost the whole of the natural world, whether as preference for a single paw or foot, or for going around in circles.

Earlier this year a report from an Australian university made newspaper headlines around the world. Dr Culum Brown and a student, Maria Magat, of Macquarie University, in Sydney, studied 322 parrots of sixteen Australian species to see which eye and claw they preferred in looking at and picking up food.

For every species except one, and in almost every bird within a species, eye and claw were matched. And in four of the species almost every bird had the same preference, with matching eye and foot.

"Ocular dominance" seems to be the key, and preference for one eye or the other is linked to which side of the brain deals with certain functions. Parrots are among the few families in nature that show as marked a handedness as humans, about eighty-nine per cent of whom (let's be accurate here) are right-handed. But while sulphur-crested cockatoos all end up left-footed, they start off in life experimenting with both claws, much like human babies. And as the left hemisphere of the brain controls the body's right side and vice versa, handedness may depend on how analysing information and control of tasks are shared and co-ordinated between the two sides of the brain.

Humans have eyes at the front and don't have to choose which one to use. But most fishes make the same choice as most birds (though diving gannets have exceptional binocular vision), and tormenting fish in tanks with scary stimuli can suggest a preference for keeping the left eye on danger. That fascinated some researchers, as the brain's right side is often involved in emotional response.

Among dogs and cats, however, paw preference seems strongly linked to gender. Research at the canine behaviour centre in the school of psychology at Queen's University Belfast by Dr Deborah Wells found the paw-use preference in fifty-three dogs was strongly linked to their sex: males preferred the left paw, females the right. Her team then turned to family cats, forty-two of them, studied in their familiar domestic settings. Invited to reach for a chunk of tuna in a jar, or a toy mouse suspended on a string, tomcats, again, preferred the left paw and females the right. (Do try this at home.)

Whales are mammals, too, and Atlantic humpbacks are under increasing study as identifiable individuals. A Woods Hole scientist, Dr Philip Clapham, has judged from scars on their jaws that eighty per cent turn on their right side when brushing along the bottom to scare up sand eels. They also use their right flippers much more in water-slapping displays. All this, he suggests, shows a measure of "population-level asymmetry" matching well with right-handedness in humans.

Most of the eleven per cent of human lefties are men. What, if anything at all, that signifies for behaviour could rashly be inferred from the work of Prof Lesley Rogers with a long-established colony of marmosets in New South Wales. The right-handed marmosets, she finds, are more adventurous, tending to rush into new surroundings and not always able to find their way out. The lefties hang back and think twice. Where that puts President Obama, who signed the visitors' book at Áras an Uachtaráin with his left hand, may properly be left to history.

June 25th 2011

The blackening boreen

On old maps of the hillside, the boreen to the shore doesn't get there, the dotted lines tilting down briefly to a pound for the townland's straying animals. Yet the track must have continued even then, a stony way for cartloads of shell sand and wrack, and for driving cattle up from a salt marsh "liable to flooding".

The boreen was still stony three decades ago, some small promise of pristine remoteness in which to venture another life. I walk most of it now before breakfast, downhill and up, in a gesture to making life last, but the arterial creep of tarmacadam has since trickled down the whole road, ending in a tourists' car park with summertime loo.

Where the dog and I splashed through the boreen's ford at the mountain river, or thrillingly, in floods, waded and swam (the dog, I mean), there now is a bridge above a concrete zero, and what is left of the stream no longer appeals to dipper or sandpiper, or the sand martins that used to nest in the banks. I stop and turn before then, at the gate of the last farm.

What gets thrown out of cars for me to pick up has changed through the years – fewer cigarette packets now, or the builders' sandwich cartons of the Tiger years. Even the number of soft-drink cans has eased, except on bank holidays when the car park fills up. This morning, as I write, sheep that turned to gaze at me wore yellow plastic earrings – tags that made them perversely individual, as sheep, perhaps, are not supposed to be.

July 2nd 2011

Water meters and me

Each morning at the same hour, in service to Met Éireann, I go out to lift the funnel from the rain gauge in the lawn, take the bottle from under it, and pour a day's raindrops into a calibrated glass tube shaped somewhat like a long crystal condom.

After many years, I can glance at the bottle and guess how many millimetres have fallen, and sometimes (not often) I am, bizarrely, correct.

There are days when the measuring glass needs to be filled twice over – 25 millimetres equals one inch – and others when the shiny meniscus of the water hovers scarcely above 0.1. On recent mornings, several little golden beetles have been swimming in the glass, so that, holding it "upright between the thumb and first finger", as instructed, and "with the surface of the water level with the eye so as to avoid errors of parallax", I can see their little legs paddling frantically to stay afloat.

I pour them out carefully, of course, but there are also mornings when, the sun flashing through the glass, I take a gulp of clear water as a toast to Gaia. Some theorists, perhaps rather way out, write of water as "a living substance", with energies and motives all of its own, and as people are two-thirds water I feel no need to argue. Living with it so intimately, from its first approach across the ocean, dissolving islands as it comes, to a final surge of the hill stream from our kitchen tap, I still find it both wilful and deeply wonderful.

The Government's plan for water charges, household meters and so on reminded me how long it had been since I followed our stream to its source. It is not, of course, "our" stream in any but the idiomatic sense, any more than the farmer through whose stripe of fields it runs would dream of denying his neighbours its benefit. Ours is just one black plastic pipe burrowing in and out of the hillside to drink from some ferny pool among the rocks.

To climb beside the stream, prompting a small scatter of sheep, is to mount into the past. Flat boulders carry little pyramids and bracelets of stones, gathered by children in clearing the land and cemented now in a matrix of wind-blown grit and lichens. Then comes a corrugation of lazy bed ridges grassed over in rounded hummocks: real giants of ridges that need a leap, one to the next.

Before the Famine, the hillside held 350 people in fifty cabins where half a dozen families live now. One farm, its old house complete with bog-deal purlins and outshot bed, held on to its lacework of drystone walls right up to the Tiger years and its erasure for a new holiday home. Even on the high land of Land Commission striping, there are foundations sunk among the rushes and tumbled remnants of walls that go nowhere.

This corner of Mayo was left bare in the last Ice Age, so one is left to guess when the glacial till, with its burden of boulders, spilled downwards from the ridge. On the way to the mountain fence, the modest summer stream chuckles at the bottom of wide ravines ten metres or more deep.

Even in white-water flood, of which we have seen many, such excavation seems excessive. Yet, where the stream crosses a corner of our acre, banks once knee deep now come up to our shoulders – this in a trivial few decades.

The purity of rain gathered up from the Atlantic should seem guaranteed, even spiced by salts and algal sulphides snatched up to make clouds. The stream sparkles through drifts of cuckoo flowers and bright blue forget-me-nots, and to drink from its water ought to be an Arcadian privilege. But beyond the mountain fence, on short-cropped commonage, sheep droppings can exceed even the legendary density of dog poo in Dalkey. Deep pools on the way are fringed with khaki-coloured filamentous algae.

Grant-aided by the county council, fine filters and ultraviolet screening in a box outside our kitchen window guard us from E coli and cryptosporidium.

The source of the stream is gathered in from a score of mossy rivulets in a pocket of bog below the ridge. I didn't quite get there, after all, as a fresh supply of juicy raindrops made it prudent to turn back.

But, so long as the stream keeps flowing, I don't quite see how we and our neighbours can be metered and taxed for leading it through our houses on its way to the sea.

Sheep shit notwithstanding, I treasure our do-it-yourself water supply and the link it sustains between us, the sea and the sky.

August 13th 2011

Healing the herbal way

Wreathed so often in mists and drizzle this summer, the moister waysides of the west are billowing with creamy meadowsweet, the soporific strewing herb of medieval bedrooms (anything to soften the pong from the privy).

Like willow, it is rich in salicylic compounds, the herbal fount of aspirin. Once, in the feverish throes of a summer flu, I bade the kitchen maid prepare a draught of meadowsweet tea. The fever broken, and blinking through the sweat, I recognised the maid to be my own dear wife, Ethna.

The trouble with such self-medication is its guesswork, and one sees the point of regulating commercial herbal remedies for quality and safety. We are regular customers of the botanical shelves in shops that sell the right, unadulterated flour for our bread and have hitherto trusted the Swiss, among others in Europe, in their distillations of remedial herbs.

We wait to see which of the familiar potions on our kitchen-shelf pharmacy will survive the EU directive on traditional herbal medicinal products, whose transitional grace for existing products expired at the end of April.

Those left unregistered with the Irish Medicines Board, and unauthorised for sale, are already beginning to disappear from health-food shops, robbed of their freelance existence as "food supplements".

The board has published two draft lists of herbal substances which may, and may not, be acceptable for inclusion in food supplements.

Of those so far approved, most are ordinary vegetables, fruits and spices, together with herbs from the wayside (burdock, yarrow, hawthorn, goldenrod, agrimony and so on) that have survived pharmaceutical reports and for which no specific medicinal claim is made on the packaging.

The list of herbs not permitted as "supplements" include obvious poisons, such as deadly nightshade, and other plants containing toxic alkaloids. But here also are herbs excluded simply because their action is pharmaceutical and thus, like any synthetic medicine, will have side effects, some of which, in some instances, may prove severe or harmful in the long term.

Rather than entrust the user with the same contraindications and warnings that come with any sheet of synthesised drugs, some herbal preparations have been abruptly curtailed. It is concerning to find that, along with echinacea, the cultivated coneflower thousands have recruited to the benefit of their immune system, and St John's wort, which has relieved a legion of the mildly depressed, I find listed my own blessed herb Serenoa repens, or saw palmetto.

This berry of a spiky palm that grows in subtropical America has, for some dozen years or more, subdued the efforts of my prostate gland to strangle my urethra, an affliction common to most ageing men and prompting frequent night-time trips to the loo.

Having found one prescribed drug too draining of energy, I discovered saw palmetto as a regular over-the-counter herbal remedy in Germany, and one that authoritative studies in the United States have judged to be perfectly safe for most men.

Saw palmetto and its herbal kin now have a home in the chemist's shop in town. As a practising pharmacist when medicine's debt to plant life was still readily on view, Ethna can only approve. (Her venerable mortar and pestle now grind coriander in the kitchen.)

But the EU directive can only regulate single herbs, while safe and successful blends evolved from generations of professional herbalism will be denied. The EU's insatiable drive for standardisation and control will mean, as herbalists argue, fewer, more costly, single herbs and a narrower spectrum of remedies.

Botany is no longer taught to medical students, but its links to drug discovery and development are still as strong as ever. It's simply that, rather than using the plants themselves when they offer novel chemicals, drug companies find ways of reproducing them synthetically on an industrial scale.

Dr Hazel Proctor of Trinity College Dublin explains this in her fascinating guide to Trinity's new Physic Garden, planted (behind the O'Reilly Building) to celebrate the college's 300 years of botany. The first botany professor, Henry Nicholson, catalogued almost 400 plants with promise of medicinal qualities. The new garden has more than seventy, many of them still in use as herbal remedies, and others that are still under current research.

Almost twenty, as it happens, are flourishing within our own acre, a few already tried to our benefit (comfrey root for bruises, yarrow tea for rheumatism, valerian for sleep) and others we'd never considered – guelder rose to prompt the immune system, sage for an ageing memory, angelica as a general feelgood tonic.

The old cottage of the healer Biddy Early, in Co Clare, is to be rescued again from the nettles: how many little blue bottles she'd have filled from stuff picked down our garden path.

August 20nd 2011
An octopus in the wild

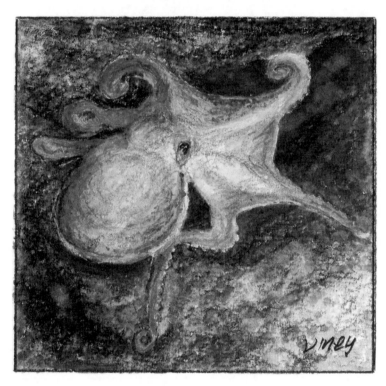

Once, when young and snorkelling off a Greek island, I dived to snatch a little octopus from the seabed, the first, and indeed the only one, I have ever seen in the wild. Left up on a jetty for closer inspection, it promptly ran across the slabs like a rubbery spider and leaped back into the sea, leaving me gaping. At least it didn't cling on and nip me, with a toxic saliva brewed for paralysing crabs, or squirt ink into my face.

The late Prof Martin Wells of Cambridge, a celebrated student of the cephalopods, warned against such kidnap of any octopus bigger than a hand's span across – "not because it intends you any harm, but because its immediate reaction when grasped is to hang on to everything within reach and clamp down".

Quite a small octopus, he declared, could hold a snorkeller underwater.

My first sight of any octopus was in Brighton, as a schoolboy. The town's venerable aquarium, beside the pier, was still in post-war disrepair, its darkness dank and dripping, the glass walls fogged with algae. The resident octopus gazed out with a listless, prisoner's eyes. The aquarium's history, however, boasts an early and startling report of an octopus escapologist. In 1875, its aquarists were puzzled by the disappearance of their lumpfish until, early one morning, the neighbouring octopus was discovered in their tank. Reports of octopuses out of the water, roving at times between rock pools, have been current since Aristotle, but how long can they survive? Up to half an hour, says WikiAnswers; ten minutes is nearer the truth.

Even today, Brighton's aquarium puts extra weights on the lid of its current octopus, Betty, and its cephalopod researcher, Kerry Perkins, has great respect for octopus resourcefulness.

She tells of one that objected to the light over its tank being left on at night and would squirt water to short-circuit it.

For that example, echoed by exploits viewable on YouTube, I am obliged to a recent New Scientist article by Caroline Williams, A Beautiful Mind. If the latest analyses are to be believed, she concluded, the assembled skills of octopuses and their invertebrate ilk (squid, cuttlefish, nautilus) in navigating mazes, differentiating shapes, solving problems, learning from each other and so on "might show a rudimentary form of consciousness". Just how rudimentary bears on a new EU regulation on animal experiments, which extends welfare provisions to cephalopods, requiring ethical evaluation of experiments causing pain, distress or lasting harm.

Researchers will have to prove that no alternative method is practical, and weigh recommendations to use analgesics or anaesthesia to prevent possible pain. They will also have to justify taking animals from the wild.

Cephalopod scientists, all for kindly provisions, have expressed worry about what these could mean for their work. How does anaesthesia affect an octopus's nervous system? Would flashing lights at cuttlefish, to see how they changed colour, be thought of as causing distress?

Prof Wells's opinions would have been blunt. A big reason for studying cephalopods is that, in an evolution diverging from that of their fellow molluscs (broadly speaking, the snail family), their brain is concentrated in the head. It is split into two halves, like ours, connected by a bundle of nerve fibres, and then divided into further specialised lobes, some folded like the human brain, packed with neurons and with plenty of storage for memory.

"Practically every darn thing we know about how nerves work," Wells said once, "has been worked out from squid nerves. That's because squids have good, big nerves you can put electrodes into." His early team experiments, testing octopus ability to distinguish, learn and remember shapes and patterns, involved repetition when the animals were blinded, or missing part of their brains.

Today's research varies widely, from chasing neuron links in living tissue (sometimes in slices in oxygenated salt water) to exploring the octopus's apparent individuality and sense of self. Many experiments employ the common European octopus, Octopus vulgaris, with its warty 70 centimetres body and two rows of stout suckers on its tentacles, which is found off Ireland's south coast.

The usual species around our shore, however, is the smaller curled octopus, Eledone cirrhosa, some 50 centimetres overall and with single rows of suckers. It lives among rocks and is occasionally stranded in rock pools at low tide – this much to the excitement of a Dún Laoghaire family, rockpooling at Seapoint in spring of last year.

August 27th 2011

Tunnel of love apples

Somewhere in the pastoral wilds of Kilkenny, in a summer long ago, the wife of a Finnish jewellery maker brought slices of tomato to the lunch table: slices half an inch thick, a hand's breadth across, jewel-bright with olive oil and scattered with chopped green basil. This simple revelation of what tomatoes should be, enfolded in mouthfuls of sweetness and scent, set my early hankering for the good life.

The current cultivation in my polytunnel of the Italian beefsteak tomato, Pantano Romanesco, thus begins on a note of deep fulfilment. That I have to grope for its fist-size fruit in a dense thicket of stems and leaves, part of it brought crashing down by sheer weight, is entirely my own doing. As the dreaded grey mould, botrytis, hovers in the dog days of late August, this is not the way to do it.

More would-be shrubs than vines, Pantano and its fellow Italians are flamboyant, gesticulating growers, throwing out multiple stems and fractal multiplications of shoots, so that order can only be kept by generous spacing, judicious feeding and assiduous daily patrols with nipping fingers. It turns out I have let them have too much their own way.

The choice of tomatoes for the home gardener has never been greater, as a network of "heirloom" seed suppliers meets the growing appetite for pre-hybrid, soft-skinned, asymmetrical, finely flavoured fruit so utterly foreign to the supermarket pack. But the commercial, billiard-ball staples can be older than we think. In my collection of such things, a Department of Agriculture leaflet on tomato growing dated 1956 has many unfamiliar names in its list – Scarlet Knight, Potentate, Victory – but also today's Ailsa Craig and Moneymaker ("the worst variety" in the view of Lawrence Hills, the English organic sage).

The department thought tomatoes were brought from South America to Europe by Christopher Columbus in 1498, but this credit is generally denied him in more modern attempts at their history. The authoritative EU-Sol agency, with the germplasm of almost 7,000 domesticated tomato lines in its collection, gets no more precise than the 1500s, and it was 1753 before Linnaeus correctly identified the plant as a species of Solanum, like the potato (and thus similarly susceptible to late blight).

Solanum lycopersicum is clearly very different from its wild predecessors in Peru, or the Atacama Desert of Chile, and the root of its common name in Mexico's ancient Aztec was an accident of trade. After Spanish conquistadores brought the plant back, southern Europeans were the first to adopt its fruit, northern Europeans being frightened off by the frequent toxicity of many well-known Solanacea (deadly nightshade, for example).

The early tomatoes were probably small, rough-skinned and yellow; those with red skins arrived much later. It is the natural red pigment in tomatoes, lycopene, that has lately acquired such a powerful reputation for human good. Over the past few decades, one scientific study after another has credited its antioxidant properties with lower risk of cancer (of the prostate, in particular) and cardiovascular disease. By a nice irony, the lycopene (one of the many beneficial carotenoids in fruit and vegetables) is most assimilable from processed tomato sauces and pastes, as in the ketchup most generally glopped on to platefuls of high-cholesterol fried food.

October 15th 2011

Why did the beetle cross the road?

An error of timing the other morning found me at the bottom of the boreen, but still severed from the strand by the deep and brimming conjunction of river and spring tide in the channel behind the dunes. It's a misjudgment that, in reverse as it were, sometimes leaves the odd and errant summer 4x4 sequestered on the far side, its occupants clustered at the water's edge in drooping disbelief: they can be left there for hours.

It was one of the quiet, pearly days of the month, not a stir in the feathery reeds along the ditch, not a murmur of traffic from the whole wide scarp of the hillside. A dilatory wheatear, pausing on a fence post, had long resumed its flight south. I turned to walk my wellingtons home again. Then the single other locus of movement on the boreen brought me to a halt. A beetle was crossing the road ahead of me.

My ageing eyesight tabbed it at once as a deargadaol, the devil's coach horse, Ocypus (sometimes Staphylinus) olens.

Where most ground beetles are glossily black – sometimes quite prettily so, with a violet sheen – the deargadaol wears the sinister matt black of a biker's leathers, the better to stalk other insects at night. As if in laddish confirmation, this one cocked its tail briefly, scorpionlike, as it trundled into the light.

It proceeded in a straight line, and at a steady speed, from one ditch to the other, before disappearing, unhurriedly, into the grass. Why, I had to wonder, did this generally nocturnal, constantly hungry and predatory creature, sheltering usually during the day under stones, logs or leaf litter, set out to cross some four metres of daylit, gravelly road quite bare of worms or woodlice? Once home, I embarked on scientific preliminaries. "Why beetle cross road?" I inquired of Google (as one does). It offered 28,400,000 discussions of the topic, all but a few of which referred to a misspelt multiple, The Beatles, and the zebra crossing outside Abbey Road Studios, in London.

This crossing appeared on the sleeve of the last album they recorded at those studios and has become a sort of shrine to the lads in their prime. Seduced to a live webcam of the scene, I found it, after forty-two years, still drawing Sunday-morning teenage fans to pose on its stripes for photographs, much to the annoyance of the city's taxi drivers.

Yes, well, otherwise…a few nice items on dung beetles, which, in a hurry to get their quite sizeable balls of dung safely away from a cowpat, may push them across a road – this, I was intrigued to see from the pictures, with their hind legs raised, which must take some doing.

But there was also, as first choice – such can be the splendid serendipity of Google – a brilliantly funny little film on YouTube. Made in the United States by Jan Skrentny in 1985, and the delight of many festivals, it offers a beetle's-eye view of the perils of crossing a road while singing under one's breath and dodging bicycle wheels, joggers and a malicious small boy with a table fork.

Thus delighted, I switched to Google Scholar for the heavy stuff.

But while scientists are great explorers of the what and how of insects, the why of the creatures' behaviour can easily disappear within the nerve-driven actions and reactions we call instincts. Self-preservation demands ultrarapid response, but here was a beetle boldly going into increased risk from, say, a watchful kestrel.

Even for rove beetles, as the deargadaol's family are known, this seemed many multiples of six steps too far (and, yes, it could have flown, just about, but the wings beneath the elytra are rarely used). Its straight-line progress towards the sun, even one hazed by cloud, was, however, typical of the sun-compass behaviour of many insects. (Some Italian shore-dwelling beetles use it to steer them away from the tide.)

As four metres of road were unlikely to offer much food, what about that other imperative, reproduction? In Skrentny's film, such a motive is finally played out to the strains of Some Enchanted Evening, and, yes, the autumn is mating time for the devil's coach horse.

Pheromones, then. The female deargadaol does, indeed, have a distinctive mix of volatile hydrocarbon compounds on its skin. But while laboratory study has male beetles exploring females with their antennae prior to mating, I have yet to find any suggestion that the female scent can be borne on the air in the manner, say, of moth pheromones, which can draw a male from fifty kilometres away. Indeed, the general failure of beetles to cross roads is widely blamed by ecologists for preventing a healthful flow of genes between the populations on either side.

My deargadaol, after all, may just have been roving hopefully.

October 22nd 2011

The beauty of lichens

Twice shorn of its leaves by this year's salty storms, the ash tree outside the window has had a difficult season.

Stripped to a basic anatomy, its trunk, biceps and knotty limbs glistening from days of ocean mist and drizzle, this muscular middleweight braces for the next round from the Atlantic.

Still far too young at twenty-one to show the ridges and fissures of old age, the tree's smooth trunk catches the eye nonetheless, its brocade of grey and old-gold lichens positively glowing on a murky autumn day. These are not the leafy or whiskery lichens that drape the west's Atlantic oakwoods but flat patches and medallions stitched in a quilt or mosaic. Some seem to be sprinkled with hidden messages or maps for hidden treasure (Graphis scripta, for example).

They are ecologically interesting, without a doubt – that tangled marriage of fungal filaments and algal cells, the pioneering reach to frosty Arctic rocks, the insistence on totally clean air – but the appeal of lichens, for me, is mainly aesthetic. Go to Paul Whelan's great website, irishlichens.ie, and enjoy the flaming discs of Caloplaca, the red-hot wands of fruiting Cladonia, the rich textures, patterns and fractal forms of Ireland's 1,000-odd species. Along with our seaweeds and wings of moths, Ireland's lichens should inspire designers of everything from high-fashion fabrics to lampshades.

In the past, when so much of natural history was the intellectual property of men, study of the lesser plants tended to be left to women.

But I like to think her pioneering work on Irish lichens gave Ballymena's Matilda Cullen Knowles (1864-1933) quite as much aesthetic as botanical satisfaction. Along with her books, the hundreds of specimens she collected and pressed set Irish lichenology on its way.

Today, we are still filling gaps in the inventories of our natural world. The thirty-two-county Lichen Ireland project, begun in 2005 and now adding in the last rarities, has amassed more than 137,200 records from 990 ten-kilometre squares.

Sponsored by environment agencies north and south of the Border, the project recruited Britain's leading lichenologists to help map the distribution of species, their laborious "square-bashing" probing every likely quarry and churchyard as well as more natural topographies of rock and bark.

Such visitors have long been drawn to the chance of rare species new to science. A trio in 1980 (Hawksworth, Coppins and James) discovered, for example, one they called Blarneya hibernica, a really quite modest lichen growing at the base of old oak trees in the southwest and resembling little blobs of squashed cotton wool.

But the state of the Irish countryside can still surprise. Neil Sanderson, a landscape ecologist with the British Lichen Society, has reported on the Lichen Ireland project in the journal British Wildlife. "The degree of disruption of the landscape in the last 400 years," he writes, "is high and all-pervasive... In most areas, finding woodland with continuity [and] veteran trees is impossible." Sanderson was impressed, nonetheless, by an "example of temperate rainforest" at Hanging Rock in Co Fermanagh, where a single old ash tree, clinging to a limestone cliff, holds Ireland's only population (so far) of a crustose, "script" lichen called Enterographa elaborata, one of a mainly tropical family with only about thirty species.

The extreme oceanic microclimate supporting rare lichens on rocks around a chain of tarns high on Mount Brandon, in Co Kerry, also, as Sanderson sees it, "mimics the ancient Celtic rainforest". A colleague, John Douglass, found similar conditions in an ancient remnant hazelwood hidden within the conifers at Ards Forest Park, in Co Donegal.

"Further exciting discoveries will certainly be made," says Sanderson.

October 29th 2011

Planespotting and cloudwatching

The first clear dawn in weeks offered most of a moon in the seaward sky and a peachy glow of sunrise behind the mountain. Out on my morning march, I lifted my eyes to an early augury of winter. Two bright contrails of transatlantic flights were converging from the ocean, each led over Mweelrea's summit by a glinting pinpoint of light. I watched as the high wind snatched at the tails of the ice plumes, whisking them away in dissipating wisps.

Strange marks on the sky have fascinated people since the Stone Age. They still worry some people of apprehensive disposition (at whose concerns I shall arrive). But vapour trails' role in making clouds is now part of the study of global warming, and the crowded sky over Ireland is a target for satellite surveillance.

Clouds trap the sun's warmth reflected from the planet. They are made by the condensation of moist air into droplets of water or ice, each with an airborne particle or aerosol at its heart.

Earth sends all kinds of natural particles and aerosol molecules into the atmosphere, to which aircraft add millions of their own.

The jet exhaust from burned kerosene pours out warm and moist gases, with sulphates, carbon soot and metal molecules, all of which condense into a linear ice cloud in the colder ambient air. In favourable conditions – typically below minus 40 degrees – a contrail can persist for several hours, grow to several kilometres long and trigger additional cirrus cloud as it spreads.

Ireland's position under the north Atlantic flight corridor means that hundreds of aircraft to and from Europe fly over the island daily at more than 24,000 feet, peaking eastwards in the early morning and westwards around noon. An Armagh Observatory study of Irish sunshine records over the century to 1998 found a fifteen per cent increase in cloud cover and a corresponding twenty per cent drop in annual sunshine. How much of this, if any, could be blamed on the modern rise in air traffic? To help study the effect of contrails on Ireland's skies, a team led by Dr Gillian Whelan of the department of geography at University College Cork, with atmospheric scientists from Germany and Nasa, has devised an automated system of sorting contrails from natural cirrus cloud by satellite thermal imaging. Tracking them through 2008, the team found contrails thickest on winter nights, with a peak at 4am. Some were exceptionally thick when compared with other studies over Europe.

Such findings, as surveillance continues, may strengthen arguments for flying at lower altitudes or changing routes to avoid sensitive masses of humid air. (But what happens to the emissions?) Contrails seen as threatening "chemtrails" have been with us as long as UFOs, and with much the same origins in widespread American social paranoia: my first alerting missive arrived from Florida almost three decades ago. People prone to believing governments are doing secret things to the world are given to watching the sky for sinister shapes in the clouds. Their suspicions are nurtured by websites, blogs and videos offering "evidence" for state or corporate conspiracy.

Early anxieties fed on rumours of cancer-causing chemicals or pathogens sifting down from contrails over American cities. More recently, the favoured "poison" has been barium, a metal element quite normally present in rainwater, but inaccurately reported in improbable concentrations on YouTube. In one Irish blog, persistent "chemtrails" are blamed for poor summers, "to make people use more gas and electricity".

My latest email on the subject comes from a teacher in Co Kildare, with "an MSc and BSc in applied physics". He is convinced that the persistent contrails he sees are, indeed, "chemtrails", intended to control climate change through geoengineering, probably at the instigation of the UN. The contrails he used to see ten years ago dissipated quickly, he points out, whereas "in 2011 they are all of a sudden forming cirrus clouds". There are days "when they literally criss-cross the sky", so their constituents must have changed. With what, he demands to know, are we being sprayed?

Just now, such concerns are intensified by projects that might, indeed, change the sky. The latest, in Britain, is Stratospheric Particle Injection for Climate Engineering, or Spice, a collaboration between researchers at the universities of Bristol, Edinburgh, Oxford and Cambridge, together with Marshall Aerospace.

It proposes raising a pipe to the stratosphere, held up by a helium balloon. Through it could be pumped a flow of suitable particles, yet to be selected, to reflect back into space a helpful few per cent of incoming solar radiation.

The first kilometre of pipe could soon rear up, cobra-like, to be filled with water as a preliminary feasibility test. "Mature and wide-ranging debate", the project's leaders agree, should explore the potential consequences. The company of internet theorists will be ready to play their part.

November 12th 2011

The growth of whalewatching

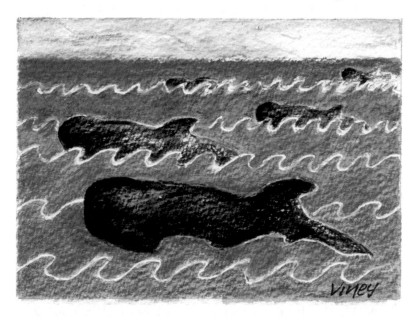

Old sea bones, like pitted stone sculptures, stand around in the sodden November tangle of my garden.

Vertebrae from a sperm whale that came ashore on the strand some seventy years ago were buried and cleansed by the sand, then disgorged after decades by winter storms.

They wear their mosses like green ermine and will crumble slowly into anonymity. The skull of a beaked whale, retrieved from a pebble spit on Hook Head, in Co Clare, lifts a fluted, lichened spire from its blind cavities.

Beachcombers are drawn on in unquenchable hope of surprise. In successive winters in the 1980s, I came upon the eighth and ninth washed-up specimens ever found in the world of True's beaked whale, Mesoplodon mirus, rarest of the smaller whales that dive for squid in the deep Atlantic. This bumper demonstration of chance was made all the more bizarre by the identification hingeing on the exact shape (oval) of the animals' only pair of teeth.

That, of course, needed the help of science – a visit by Prof James Fairley, then of NUI Galway, who chopped off the significant tip of the jaw with his little red hatchet, and later by Terry Bruton, now curator of mammals at the Ulster Museum. He bravely excavated a whole corpse in blubbery chunks, for later assembly of its skeleton, watched by my farming neighbours standing well upwind.

Such mortuary detail helps to make the point that, until a mere couple of decades ago, virtually all we knew of the variety and distribution of the whales and dolphins around Ireland was judged from the catches of a short-lived Norwegian whaling station in north Co Mayo in the early twentieth-century and years of random recording, at the back of the Irish Naturalists' Journal, of cetacea stranded, mostly dead, along our shores.

There were hints, from time to time, of the exciting live sightings waiting at sea. Dr Peter Evans of Oxford University, encountering his first whale – a fin – off the Old Head of Kinsale, went home to found a cetacean group, in 1973, within the UK Mammal Society.

In Ireland, things took a bit longer. But, twenty-one years ago, a group of about thirty people met at the newly opened office of Enfo, in Dublin.

They were brought together by Brendan Price, now best known for his dedicated work on saving seals, who was proposing that Irish waters be declared an international whale sanctuary. This was ultimately acted on by Charles Haughey, but the meeting also created the Irish Whale and Dolphin Group.

Recording stranded whales and dolphins is still its core activity, and the number reported (duly photographed and measured) to its website (iwdg. ie) has steadily increased to about 120-140 a year. Harbour porpoises lead in number, followed by common dolphin and then striped, bottlenose or white-sided dolphin, or minke whale. But the living whales and dolphins of Ireland, leaping out of the ocean with what can pass so persuasively for joy, are now part of the nation's popular culture, shared from whale watching boats or clifftops, or on television. The seasonal parade of feeding fin whales and humpbacks along the south coast, discovered in marathon telescope watches by Pádraig Whooley of the Irish Whale and Dolphin Group, is new knowledge of international interest, adding to spectacular sightings of sperm whales and even blue whales – the world's biggest animal – out near the edge of the continental shelf.

A humpback whale was once considered a great rarity off Ireland's coasts, yet observing them is now a regular pleasure. After almost fifteen weeks of sightings since July, Nick Hassett was still watching a pair off the Dingle Peninsula late in October, conjuring bubble nets from their blowholes to trap shoals of herring.

With humpbacks now individually identified from the patterning of their tail flukes (those off Kerry were HB IRL 10 and 15), new knowledge about migration and breeding is added every year. The gift of Haughey's yacht, Celtic Mist, equips the Irish Whale and Dolphin Group for even more systematic observation.

But, as Dr Simon Berrow, founder member and co-ordinator of the group, has asked, are cetaceans and their habitats any better protected now than before the group was formed? As a scientist, he can't answer: that needs evidence. Were the whales and dolphins always there offshore, just waiting to be watched by people? It seems incredible that, with a trawler fleet so busy off the south and west coasts, the regular migrations should not have been remarked on – yet equally improbable that the animals have warmed, as it were, to Ireland's benign intentions.

At least, thanks to the Irish Whale and Dolphin Group, they are now part of what we know and love about the natural world.

December 10th 2011
My father: sailor, sower, grower

Harry Viney, my father, cut a trapdoor in the floorboards to give access to the space where our house was raised from the earth. This mini-cellar was not deep enough to stand up in, so that I, being young, was sent down with a torch to retrieve his potatoes, parsnips and carrots. There was a sweet, fungal smell of damp hempen sacks and the minute-to-minute fear of spiders.

Today's terraced houses seem not to have floorboards downstairs any more, and claiming the nearest derelict street corner for an allotment might not seem appropriate in peacetime. But today I think of Harry, with his baldy head and all the skills he brought to the family in the hard years of war. Born in rural Hampshire, apprenticed to the village carpenter at twelve, he carried a whole kit of aptitudes through a life that found, for a decade or two, some comfort, and then, as times changed, called for more.

He mended our shoes on a heavy steel last, carving new soles from a big sheet of leather, and plucking brads for the hammer from the row between his lips. He made new clothes from old, marking out the lines with a disc of tailor's chalk and whirring away at the Singer sewing machine. Once, coming by fabric from a grounded barrage balloon, he made me a new raincoat and a satchel for school, bestowing on a ten-year-old a silvery and unwelcome singularity.

A spell as a marine in the first World War taught him the virtues of the sailor's ditty bag, with needles, thread and string. Also, a way of binding things tightly with cord, binding his allotment-grown, molasses-soaked tobacco into big cigars, to be shaved with a penknife for his pipe. It was, undeniably, tobacco, but smelled like green nettles on a bonfire.

In his post-war old age, pensioned off from housepainter's ladders, he obtained an old perambulator and took it to the Undercliff Walk, where he gathered driftwood and brought it home to dry. Then he sawed it and chopped it up into firewood and began selling it in bundles as kindling for coal fires, door to door. His younger son, upwardly mobile as a scholarship boy, begged him not to be so bloody embarrassing, Dad, and he complied.

Apart from such filial guilts, this month, as I was ordering seed potatoes for next spring, seemed a good time to offer the story of Harry. Not that one expects too many fathers to have his range of talents, but doing it yourself can range more widely than stylish use of an electric screwdriver: it's the the spirit that counts.

January 28th 2012
A blackbird on my hawthorn

A southeast wind has to squeeze through the mountains, first Connemara's Twelve Bens and then the Sheefrys and Mweelrea on our side of the bay. At gale force, the wind can emerge in bullying, even frightening, gusts, but at other more steady, if still wintry, volumes it just plays games with the clouds.

"Where stable, moist air flows over a mountain or a range of mountains" – this from Wikipedia – "a series of large-scale standing waves may form on the downwind side. If the temperature at the rest of the wave drops to the dew point, moisture in the air may condense to form lenticular clouds…Under certain conditions, long strings of lenticular clouds can form near the crest of each successive wave." Thus, at dawn the other morning, with the summit of Mweelrea lost in a cloud of its own, a whole line of UFOs – lenticular = lens-shaped, as you knew – trailed away across the sea, each gauzy saucer gilded by the rising sun. Even with Wikipedia's meteorology on tap, I felt a druidic shiver of delight.

Must science always intrude on magic, begging for explanations? On the UFO morning, a cock blackbird was singing from the summit of a hawthorn bush, its bill the same bright gold as the cloud above the mountain. The full territorial concerto, fluent, supple and elaborate, held me marvelling as I stooped above the rain gauge.

But again, of course, the questions insisted: how much instinct, how much learning and choice? The literature on birdsong began with Aristotle – "In general, the birds produce most voice, and with most variety, when they are concerned with mating" – and has proceeded in modern times, via the sono-gram, to ever-more refined acoustic and behavioural deconstruction.

The male blackbird, indeed, now has a literature all his own. Much of it currently reports on the research of Dr Torben Dabelsteen, an evolutionary biologist at the University of Copenhagen who probes the purpose, structure and effect of the cock blackbird's song and evolution's selection of its qualities for defending territories, winning mates and so on. With postgraduate teams to help, he uses acoustic gadgetry in blackbird woods and gardens to intervene in the birds' dawn chorus and see how individuals respond.

"If I were a blackbird, I'd whistle and sing…" The whistling that launches the blackbird's territorial song is a far-carrying "omnidirectional" announce-

139

ment, meant for other cocks, and the twittering that often ends it is for strictly local consumption, a measure of excitement intended, perhaps, for females listening in the undergrowth. The main melody is meant for other males, but is by no means a standard performance. Indeed, the Danes had to analyse more than 200 songs to estimate a male's repertoire, which averaged forty-four different musical phrases, or motifs.

Most of these are learned by young birds from communal song, but while many start-up motifs are shared between the birds, perhaps a dozen in the middle are highly individual and perfected by practice. Entire songs are only occasionally repeated, but these motifs are always sung in the same order.

Theory supported by several studies had predicted that the size of a cock blackbird's repertoire lets potential rivals judge each other's fighting ability – "an honest signal of male quality", as the Danes put it.

Indeed, Dabelsteen had already found a match between body size and size of song. So this might be important for natural selection of the "fittest" birds, not only for male-male competition but also for female choice of a mate.

In 2010, on the German island of Heligoland, there were eighty breeding pairs of blackbirds. In "a territory intrusion playback experiment", Dabelsteen's team removed some of the territorial males and installed loudspeakers in their place.

These broadcast recorded songs of different repertoires and sizes and assessed the responses of neighbouring cocks. To Dabelsteen's surprise, they didn't seem to tell one from another: size, after all, wasn't everything.

That won't, of course, be the end of it.

Female canaries, apparently, choose males with "sexy syllables" that take a lot of energy to produce. Perhaps it's some of these, embedded in the blackbird's individual phrases, that come to matter most in the nest.

My blackbird, as it happens, was singing all alone, not even bothering to twitter before diving back down from his perch on the hawthorn. Maybe he was just rehearsing ahead of time – perhaps led astray in January by three fine days together and my alexanders, a Mediterranean herb, already in tentative bloom.

Nothing seems all that extraordinary now, not even a sky full of jellyfish, UFOs or gilded, lenticular clouds.

April 21st 2012

Our first nesting rooks

The mellifluous twittering of songbirds that attends my seed-sowing sessions in the polytunnel was rudely drowned out the other morning by a clamour of harshly disputatious noises from one of the trees that give the tunnel its shelter.

Our first nesting rooks were reminding me that they can make very noisy neighbours.

Would we really welcome any more? At the time their tall sycamore was planted, about thirty years ago, a colony of some fifty pairs nested each year in the old sycamores around the farmhouse down the hill.

I could peer into the rookery as if into a Neolithic village, a circle of spiky nests wreathed in turf smoke from the chimney.

The birds' grand, wheeling processions against the afterglow of the ocean sunset were special of their kind.

Yet it was no great surprise when the rookery, erupting into raucous discourse as early as 4am, was eventually persuaded to vacate the farmstead, or for me to find that young men from such houses tend to build a new one of their own without wanting a tree in sight.

The many rookless years at least spared us the birds' dawn raids on our potato ridges – a complaint, I note, shared by the Tipperary nuns who, in the War of Independence more than ninety years ago, beseeched the British army to come and shoot the birds. (Their letter will be auctioned in Dublin this coming Wednesday.) The role of rooks on farmland – damaging, beneficial or both – has inspired a lot of research. Against their keen appetite for leatherjackets (the big, root-chewing grubs of the crane fly) and other insect pests, one must count the birds' banqueting on fresh-sown grain or cereals in cornfields lodged by bad weather.

Irish farmers now complain that rooks tear holes in the shiny black plastic stretched over their bales of silage; some even paint big white noughts or crosses on the bales as a charm or communal deterrent.

A Teagasc survey found birds – mostly rooks – guilty of damaging bales on sixty-three per cent of Irish farms, leaving their droppings and footprints on the plastic and, by letting in the air, making the silage go mouldy. It made no conjecture on the birds' motivation.

Nor did it offer any relationship between the incidence of bird damage and the presence or absence of rookeries – small rookeries are abundant throughout the well-hedged farming countryside, and virtually all baled silage is within reach.

The definitive study of Irish rooks is still one carried out twenty years ago by a young Scottish ornithologist, Ron Macdonald, for his PhD. A mark of his industry was a count of about 5,000 nests in sixty-six rookeries in 100 square kilometres of Co Kildare.

Bringing technology to bear with something called (gloriously) an automatic adiabatic bomb calorimeter, he was able to show that, for a rook, one acorn packs as much energy as about thirty small earthworms (which is why they hide them as a takeaway reserve).

A typical rookery in Ireland might contain only a couple of hundred rooks, whereas some of those on the Continent have populations of thousands. They all, I suppose, have to start with one pair building an isolated nest, though single nests such as we have seem to be rare.

What, then, was the row about when I was in the tunnel? A subsequent rúisc of cawing soon after sunrise drew my binoculars to the treetop, where two rooks were whirling in a flurry of wings and a third – the female – was slipping back into the nest to sit on her eggs.

The intruder retreated (perhaps for the umpteenth time), and the resident male resumed his perch as sentinel.

A UK study of rook breeding behaviour suggests a tabloid scenario. The posture of an incubating female can, it seems, be misinterpreted as solicitation by an unengaged and randy male.

Attempts at copulation occur most frequently, indeed, between birds that are not paired to each other and most often with an incubating female. They are usually countered by the rightful spouse – but imagine this carry-on in a colony of fifty nests.

Ireland's rooks seem safe enough in numbers. Those in the North, indeed, actually doubled in the late 1990s, and Co Derry has the highest density of nesting rooks in these islands.

April 28th 2012
The bees and the beans

The tallest plants in the tunnel just now are the thicket of broad beans (var Aquadulce) sown last autumn.

Fired up by pelleted chicken manure and an early blast of sun, their whorls of bold black, white and pink flowers are swaying shoulder high, while the first pods are swelling from their shrivelled predecessors lower down the stems. I've never had such a promising crop – nor learned so much about one plant and its wildlife.

The beauty of a polytunnel is getting to sit down in the warm and watch things. There's the robin, when it trusts me, and soon the odd butterfly, but when the beans began to flower I was looking out for bumblebees.

Broad beans will fertilise themselves: the night before the flowers open, the anthers inside are already shedding pollen that can reach the stigma. But a proper, cross-pollinating job between plants needs the forcible entrance of a hairy, nectar-thirsty bumblebee. There are tests to show that plants caged with bees produce longer pods with more and heavier beans than plants caged without bees.

The queen bumblebees of early spring have considerable aerial presence. I welcomed the first through the open tunnel door in early March, making – what else? – a beeline for the first clusters of bean flowers. But hey! This was no good. Instead of entering the open blossoms it perched at the back of their bells and bit through the petals to suck up the nectar within.

To regular bean-watchers, this is old news.

There are bumblebees with short tongues and others with long ones. The white-tailed Bombus lucorum and the even bigger Bombus terrestris are both short-tongued. Unable to reach the nectar from the front, they are notorious nectar robbers around the back, not only with beans but also with honeysuckle, comfrey and other flowers.

This can leave the common garden bumblebee, Bombus hortorum, unfurling its long tongue into more and more flowers, which could actually be good for bean-making.

As bee visitors built up among my beans, I was cheering on the ones that chose the flowers' front door.

Next came the great ant mystery. Veterans of this column may remember that the ants in my tunnel are not welcome. They are testy wood ants, quick to spray acid on my skin and raising big, allergic bumps that itch for days. I am trying to control them with various sinister means, but there they were, mooching around the higher reaches of my beans.

A particular insect pest of broad beans, familiar to many gardeners, is infestation by black aphids, or blackfly, multiplying explosively and sucking the sap of the growing shoots. In a phenomenon found worldwide, ants feed on the sugary liquid – honeydew – that exudes from bums of aphids, green or black. Finding this an excellent food, the ants look after the aphids, farming them like cattle, moving them around on plants and protecting them from predators. EO Wilson, world expert on ant society, sees this as an evolutionary arrangement, beneficial to both insects.

My beans, however, have no black aphids (and never had, come to that). So were the ants just hanging around, hoping for some to arrive? I fetched a magnifying glass to watch them more closely. I found them, singly and in pairs, sucking away at small black spots, the size of a match head, beneath leafy axils on the stems. Were these an advance guard of black aphids? However hard I looked, the spots didn't move, or have legs.

An hour later I was still online in my study, tuned to Google Scholar and fascinated by something quite new to me, even though its discovery dates to 1762. Many plants, all over the world, tropical orchids and hibiscus among them, are not content to draw insects by offering nectar in their flowers. They also have features called "extrafloral nectaries", such as the little black spots on my beans.

They are there to bring hordes of ants ("pugnacious bodyguards" in the title of one paper) to protect the plants against insect predators or parasites. It is, supposedly, another evolutionary symbiosis – plants and insects have evolved together in many mutually beneficial ways. But if black aphids arrive on the beans and the ants protect them, where is the pay-off for the plants? Evolutionary biologists are still picking at a global puzzle that extends to pugnacious ants and tropical leaf-hoppers, caterpillars and bud-destroying wasps. Perhaps the extrafloral nectaries on broad beans (originally from North Africa) divert the ants from the aphids' honeydew, leaving them to be reduced by predation by ladybird larvae. So much in nature is a delicate balance of odds.

There is another story about broad beans (or fava beans as much of the world calls them), involving a genetic disorder that makes them a dangerous food for some Mediterranean communities. This explains why, asking Google Scholar for "ants fava beans", it also offered work containing "peasants", "variants" and "descendants."

May 5th 2012
Dandelion wine

The yellow of dandelions is like no other, that glow of orange at the heart of the flower surely borrowed from the sun. The verges of our western roads have been swathed in dandelion gold this spring, and soon the traffic will whisk another ghostly blizzard of seed to the farthest ribbons of tarmac.

Dandelions seem, indeed, to get pretty well everywhere. The mammoth New Atlas of the British & Irish Flora shows them growing solidly right across the UK, thinning out only in the Scottish Highlands above 1,220 metres. Ireland, it seems, has many more patches of dandelion-free landscape in bogs, on mountain tops and on the barer reaches of the Burren.

My own little crop lights up odd corners of the garden, but the readiness of sheep to graze on dandelions keeps the surrounding hillside quite free of them.

I've been thinking of all the lawns created by the thousands of families newly settled on Leinster farmland. Most of the new lawns will be made on topsoil of uncertain origin, which leaves its burden of wild seeds a matter of luck.

The soil beneath permanent pasture closely grazed for many years is relatively free of weed seeds, but little of eastern grassland has been left unploughed, if only for reseeding with ryegrass and clover. Old cereal fields are another matter, and the seeds of arable weeds can stay viable in the soil for as long as fifty-eight years.

In any case, dandelions are born pioneers, delighting in disturbed soil, which is what a new lawn starts out as. Their actual abundance in established city lawns is often far below that of white clover, daisies and creeping buttercup.

In the newer dormitory estates, the list of weeds ahead of dandelions gets longer: yarrow, plantain and the lovely blue-flowered self-heal may be part of the original inheritance of seeds. But Taraxacum agg is still the plant that seems to spark the lawn-maker's fiercest shame.

What is this agg? Isn't the basic dandelion species Taraxacum officinale, the so-to-speak "official" plant of botany, herbalism and the index of innumerable wild flower books? Not exactly: agg is short for aggregate. In its proliferating microspecies – more than seventy so far recorded in Co Dublin alone, with probably many more to come – the humble dandelion is, indeed, as the new Webb's An Irish Flora confirms, "a very difficult genus", its flowers not always

145

to be told apart, even in the hand.

The American ecologist Paul Ehrlich once described the reproductive pol-icy of dandelions as "perhaps the greatest mystery in the world of plant sex". Despite their brilliant cushions of florets and the offering, in early spring, of nectar sought by bumblebees and hoverflies, they set seeds entirely asexually – without pollination and fertilisation – and never, therefore, interbreed. The environmental shaping of the microspecies, and their genetic persistence, is a continuing challenge for students of floral evolution.

The lacy globe of the dandelion clock is an exquisite piece of flower engi-neering, all of a piece with the plants' invisible wheels and cogs and calcula-tions. One set responds to changes in light, in fine weather stretching the florets to the sun and following its course across the sky, or closing the head up as soon as rain threatens, opening also for sunrise and closing at evening.

Another set of invisible pulleys keep the plant in proper shape.

Each year it produces new leaves at the top of its rosette, and every now and then the taproot contracts to pull the rosette downwards. This keeps the new leaves at ground level, spread to smother competing plants, gather the light and steer every raindrop straight to the root.

Such a ubiquitous plant group (thought to have arisen in the west Hima-layas when dinosaurs were still grazing) has a long history of human herbal exploration. "Dandelion" is a corruption of the French dent-de-lion, which is turn echoed its old Latin name, dens leonis. In most European languages the flower's name means the same thing – lion's tooth – but the Irish caisearb-han (bitter stalk) is somewhat more germane. Pissenlit (pissy beds), also in French, speaks for the plant's best-known property, but studies continue for its medicinal potential, whether diuretic, anti-inflammatory, anti-oxidative, anti-carcinogenic, analgesic, anti-coagulatory or prebiotic.

I think, rather, of dandelion wine, a favourite tipple of my country-born mother and still brewed by her after long years in town. I picked her buckets of the flowers in spring, a gallon for each gallon of wine, and found quite the best harvest between the old, lime-white tombs of the churchyard at the top of the hill.

She fermented the flowers with lemons and raisins (for tannin) in a big earthenware crock under the stairs. The smell that crept out at this time was mysteriously dark and pungent, but the wine at Christmas brought a sip of spring.

May 26th 2012

Cold winters, no chats

In the gentle spring soundtrack that ushers me along the boreen these mornings (the better mornings, that is), one sound has been missing from the general blend of birdsong, sea breeze and disassembling surf from the shore. Norman MacCaig had a nice phrase for it – "a flint-on-flint ticking" – but the stonechat's own name says it well enough.

MacCaig also found praise for "a tiny work of art / Bright as an illumination on a monkish parchment", and that is the other reason I miss this little bird. It used to keep me company as I marched, bouncing along the fence ahead of me, post by post along its nesting territory, the bold black head, white collar, rosy breast as pert and assertive as its scolding call.

But when did it vanish and why? The questions were sharpened by an email from Wexford. Michael Lunt, a lifelong birder, has missed the stonechat both from his local fields and from those of Connemara. Nothing much has changed in habitats where it was common – coastal farmland with plenty of gorse or scrub – so its sudden absence was baffling.

Chats are scaled-down thrushes; that, at least, is their ornithological family. Nothing in build or diet seems to put the resident, insect-eating stonechat at a special disadvantage, and our most populous and widespread chat, the robin, is surely a born survivor. The stonechat's continent-wide decline in Europe is just part of the general loss of birds brought about by intensive farming, but a sudden, dramatic disappearance needs extra explanation.

A study for the British Trust for Ornithology offered it some fifty years ago: stonechats are in trouble in really hard winters. The author, JD Magee, listed a series of severe British winters with dire impacts on the species, culminating in the memorable blizzards of my childhood in 1946-47.

"After this winter," wrote Magee, "stonechats were greatly reduced even in Cornwall, one of the strongholds of the species, no breeding birds could be found anywhere in south Wales…The populations of eastern and central Scotland were also almost wiped out." The birds crept back in coastal areas, but in Suffolk, on England's east coast, a slight increase took four years. Before our recent two harsh winters, BirdWatch Ireland's countryside bird survey could report that the stonechat, like the goldfinch, had "increased substantially over the past 10 years". This may now need updating.

The stonechat's apparent vulnerability to cold is in striking contrast to the story of another chat, the wheatear. In March, even before the swallows returned, a male wheatear from Africa was chacking away from its usual perch on a boulder in the field beyond my window. Oenanthe oenanthe is a regular migrant to the west of Ireland (and uplands farther inland), nesting happily in stone walls and rabbit burrows and flashing the white rump that prompted "white arse" as its Anglo-Saxon name.

However, spring wheatears spotted on a coastal shingle bank, or feeding on a headland or island, may not be breeding here, but could be travelling immensely farther. They may be flying on to Canada, or even beyond, to Alaska – an incredible 14,500 kilometres from their wintering grounds south of the Sahara. The full range of the "Greenland wheatear", as this race or subspecies is generally known (leucorrhoa is sometimes tacked on to its name), is now confirmed by new tracking devices, weighing little more than a gram, fitted to birds that themselves weigh a mere twenty-five grams.

The two kinds of wheatear seem scarcely different in the field, but the long-distance migrants have pointed wings six or seven millimetres longer, their bills are imperceptibly heavier, and the buff of the breast and the brown of the back are distinctly richer in hue. When I came across them once in northeast Greenland, they were just another delightful surprise.

On the northward migration, they often take the journey in stages, pausing to rest and feed in Ireland, Scotland and Iceland: arriving in the Arctic too early, they too might succumb to the cold. Flying back in autumn with their young, some birds use the same route, passing through Ireland mainly in September. But many use northwesterly winds to fly from Greenland to Europe in a single passage over more than 3,000 kilometres of sea.

Migration, on routes becoming longer over centuries as the last ice retreated, is a product of natural selection, and flying to "empty" regions full of insect food leads to greater breeding success. The late Peter Conder, a director of the Royal Society for the Protection of Birds, devoted a book to the wheatear in 1989, more than twenty years ahead of today's high-tech tracking. "I am sure," he wrote, "that this enormous expenditure of energy…in order to raise five young does balance out."

June 9th 2012

Comfrey the wonderdrug

The budgeting of energy that arrives with advancing age has made certain inroads on my organic aspirations. Buckets of pelleted chicken manure, its veterinary provenance unclear, have supplanted the loads of free and fragrant seaweed from the shore. Many paths and non-crop areas are tamed with herbicide spray.

And while canopies of fine net protect the outside vegetables against root fly and caterpillars, my ceaseless war on slugs has sometimes succumbed to the chemical road. Manual slug hunts by torchlight, as urged by the saints, have merely confirmed that there are millions more molluscs where those came from.

But some old loyalties remain, among them faith in comfrey, the "wonder" herb. As a supermanure, as fodder for livestock and as miracle balm for fractures and bruises, this big, hairy relative of borage and forget-me-not has become an icon of organic orthodoxy. The offer of rooted cuttings in the glossiest of this year's seed catalogues shows just how far things have come since the ridicule of "sandals, beards and muesli" of only a few decades ago.

The cuttings, moreover, are for the strain of Russian comfrey known as Bocking 14, acknowledging the need to grow the right stuff.

Comfrey, Symphytum officinale, is a widespread plant of Ireland's damp and grassy waysides. But Russian comfrey, championed by a nineteenth-century Quaker called Henry Doubleday, is a cross with rough comfrey, Symphytum asperum, and Bocking 14 is the super-large-leafed cultivar Symphytum uplandicum, developed at Bocking in Britain in the 1950s by the late Lawrence Hills, a guru of the modern organic movement.

The leading virtue of Bocking 14 is less its big leaves than its hybrid sterility. Comfrey, rather like horseradish, can be a plant one has forever, any lost fragment regenerating, triffid-like, from the soil. Viable seeds would merely encourage its spread. Back in our pioneering days, I forked out for a bundle of roots on offer from blow-ins in Co Clare, hoping for a bargain lot of Bocking and a great source of fodder for our goats. As they were allowed to flower for the bumblebees and later to set seed, however, the passage of thirty years or so finds new plants scattered in self-sown clumps and thickets among my vegetable beds; indeed, they will turn up almost anywhere. But I have just stuffed a wheelbarrowload of leaves into a plastic dustbin with a cork at the bottom.

Pressed down under a weight, they will squeeze out a trickle of smelly black juice, rich in phosphate, for the tunnel's tomatoes.

Comfrey's fertilising chemistry – the "natural mineral wine" as Hills called it – is enriched from roots as deep and greedy as a tree's. For the details of its NPK – nitrogen, phosphorus and potassium – rating and so on, there are plentiful sources online. The plant's lavish and irrepressible growth allows a harvest (with gloves and shears) several times a year. But comfrey can do more than prime the growth of food crops, and today's clinical trials of its therapeutic uses are confirming what herbalists had known since Dioscorides.

Knitbone, bruisewort, boneset – the common English names of comfrey – speak for its power to take down the swelling around fractures and strains. In Irish, meacan dubh, or black root, focuses on the plant's most potent source of relief, and lus na gcnámh briste says it all. In our corner of Mayo a few people know meacan dubh as a herb "the old people" used to value, but even fewer know that this is comfrey or what it was used for.

Even Niall Mac Coitir's encyclopaedic Irish Wild Plants: Myths, Legends & Folklore (2006), surprisingly, missed its herbal history.

We soon came to prize comfrey not only as goat fodder but also as a salve for stings and bites and the bumps and bruises of the smallholder's life. The root, in particular, is rich in mucilage and in allantoin, a cell proliferant and anti-inflammatory once listed officially in British Pharmacopoeia, the handbook of pre-blister-pack chemists.

Our daughter hobbled home once when young, leading her pony and crying with pain: Báinín had stepped on her plimsolled foot. The bruise above her toes was black and swollen, but a poultice of macerated comfrey had it fading within hours. In Phytomedicine, an international science journal, "a double-blind, multicentre, randomised, placebo-controlled group comparison study" on patients with acute ankle sprains confirmed the efficacy of comfrey ointment, as did a comparable trial on 220 patients with chronic and painful osteoarthritis of the knee.

There may be bounds to the plant's healthful benefits. Having produced cancer in the livers of young laboratory rats, comfrey was once classed as a potential poison in Australia, thus appalling the thousands of people there and in Europe who were happily eating its shoots in salads or drinking comfrey tea. But comfrey seems to have outlived this controversy, as it outlives almost everything else.

June 16th 2012

A highly prized plague fish

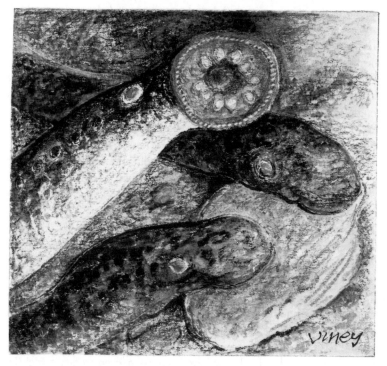

"Tiny wasps are known whose larvae parasitize the larvae of still other kinds of wasps that live inside the bodies of the caterpillars of certain species of moths that feed on certain kinds of plants that live on other plants." Edward O Wilson offered this tangle in The Diversity of Life as an ultimate in customised dependence among the myriad parasites of nature.

They include, of course, the large community of organisms – skin mites, bacteria, fungi and sometimes worms and lice – adapted to live on or in the human body.

Some parasites do ultimately kill their hosts, as in the microscopic nematode worms bought by many organic gardeners to control pest insects. But most succeed in eating their hosts sustainably – "one small piece at a time", in Wilson's phrase. In the case of the lampreys of our rivers and lakes, the human distaste for their method doesn't quite spoil the interest of their lives and history.

In Co Limerick just now, at the Annacotty bridge on the River Mulkear, a tributary of the Shannon, one apparently stands a good chance of watching dozens of sea lampreys building their nests with stones on the riverbed below.

They can move quite large ones, twice the size of a fist, with the suckers beneath their noses.

These circular mouths, studded with rasping teeth, have a certain disturbing likeness to the giant machines that bore tunnels, such is nature's inspiration to engineering design.

Petromyzonidae, or "stone suckers", is actually the lampreys' family name, but the mouth is also used to excavate blood and muscle tissue from the flanks of fish met in rivers or sea – mostly merely wounding but sometimes grinding too far. Thus, in one part of the world, lampreys can be prized and conserved as a vulnerable wild species while in another they are reckoned a devastating plague.

The fascination begins with their place in evolution. The eel-like lampreys, too slippery to hold, are jawless fish. And while near relatives are the hagfish – squirming bundles that recycle dead whales on the deep seabed – lampreys have backbones of cartilage, which make them vertebrates. Indeed, the jawless fish, Agnatha, are reckoned the oldest vertebrates of all, emerging on the evolutionary tree hundreds of millions of years ago, precursors of the human form.

Ireland has three species of lamprey – sea, river and brook, in descending size – and while in England they have been eaten, even to fatal surfeit by Henry I in 1135, it took the EU habitats directive to generate much interest on this island. Commanding special areas of conservation for lampreys, it has warranted river-by-river studies for the National Parks and Wildlife Service, with electrofishing, snorkelling and radio tracking.

Only sea and river lampreys are anadromous, moving between the ocean and their spawning grounds in rivers; the smaller brook lampreys were cut off by Ireland's postglacial rise. As in Europe and Britain, the main hazard to lamprey populations here is weirs and other obstacles between estuaries and spawning rivers. Their larvae spend up to eight years buried in silt and feeding on diatoms.

Along with parts of the Suir, Nore and Moy, the lower Shannon is especially important for sea lampreys. The Annacotty stretch of the Mulkear is the focus of monitoring and conservation, even to the point of building special passes at the weir. The website mulkearlife.com gives the story of a remarkable venture to conserve not only lampreys but also otters and salmon. Lampreys do sometimes chew on laggardly salmon but balance things out ecologically by cleaning up gravel for the salmon to spawn on in autumn.

The story across the Atlantic is strikingly different. Sea lampreys, native to North America's east coast rivers, have become an invasive species in the Great Lakes. Reaching them through shipping canals in the 1920s, they have preyed heavily on commercial fish stocks and left anglers complaining of catches "like Swiss cheese". The US government spends about $14 million a year on chemicals, traps and electric barriers in spawning streams, and releases thousands of chemically sterilised males to engage in unproductive mating.

Lampreys are perfectly good to eat – think of smoked eel: delicious – and both Sweden and Finland have major fisheries for river lampreys, caught in basket traps on migration upstream. The UK had a fishery on the River Severn, and its lampreys once went into the decorated pie presented to the monarch by the city of Gloucester on big royal occasions.

The habitats directive has changed all that, and the lampreys for Queen Elizabeth's diamond-jubilee pie were a gift flown in from Lake Huron. "I'd have sent them truckloads," said a spokesman for the Great Lakes Fisheries Commission.

June 23ʳᵈ 2012

A mouse in the tunnel

The first brown rat I ever watched was dining at our bird table on a sunny morning. It looked the very picture of health, each hair shampooed and shining, its little ears perked up in furry shells. It sat comfortably poised on its haunches, holding an oat flake daintily between its paws like child making a biscuit last. Its eyes sparkled, its whiskers trembled in the breeze.

Only that scaly, naked tail remained unforgivable.

Encounters since then have had a different and shuddersome tempo: the rat leaping across my hand from its tunnel in the compost heap, or the one in the airing cupboard, diving back to its escape route down among the boulders on which our house is set. How sad that rodents lose their innocence whenever they get too close.

In the tunnel the other morning, a rustle in the jungle of courgette plants froze me in mid-step. Perhaps a wren? But what crept out from beneath the great saffron blossoms was a house mouse on its holidays.

Oblivious to my hulking silhouette, he reached up to find another seed among the starry flowers of chickweed – put little trousers on him and he could have posed for Beatrix Potter.

Gardeners do not actually welcome mice into their polytunnels. In her new and engaging memoir, Just Vegetating (Frances Lincoln, £18.99), Joy Larkcom lists a New Year's resolution – "I will set mousetraps under cloches before sowing peas" – and from her greenhouse at Clonakilty, Co Cork, describes toasting the cheese with a lighted match to give it more flavour.

My father used to roll his peas in red lead to discourage thieving field mice (it worked, and we lived), but I go to the trouble of raising young plants in lots of yogurt pots perched high on slippery-sided plastic buckets, then setting them out in the ground. I will deal with the mouse (perhaps, indeed, mice) in due course, but meanwhile have been fascinated by its restless energy and lack of caution in broad daylight, sidling round my wellies to reach the next clump of chickweed, or munching along a seed head of grass as if it were a cob of sweetcorn.

A sad irony is that, while Mus musculus domesticus has quite deserted our house for the summer warmth of the polytunnel, its country cousin the field mouse, Apodemus sylvaticus, persists in sneaking underground to reach the cupboard under the kitchen sink, where a mousetrap waits next to the scraps bucket. Four in a row so far this month, each briefly mourned (they're lovable), have been slung regretfully over the hedge for stoat or kestrel to dine on.

More is known about Mus domesticus than about any other mammal except us. There are at least five European and two Asian species lumped under the same name and another fourteen Asian species in the same genus. A lot of them live wild for a lot of the time, but the west European subspecies of house mouse seems to have stuck with people and to need large human settlements to multiply.

A recent genetic study of British and Irish house mice found a major lineage of mitochondrial DNA (handed down through females) restricted to the northern and western peripheries of these islands and occurring also in Norway. What has been termed the Orkney mouse probably arrived here with the Vikings and would certainly have thrived in a medieval Dublin floored with woodchips, nutshells, spilt fodder and dung and since described as "a very large and rich compost heap…more than three metres deep".

From such imported ancestry sprang local communities of Irish mice, their genetic divergence increasing with distance and their wide variation in coat colour encouraging all sorts of speculation about subspecies, even into the twentieth century. A celebrated variation was the sandy-brown coat of house mice living not on some far-flung western dune system but on Bull Island in Dublin Bay.

In the 1930s a mammalogist known as Eugene "Bugs" O'Mahony studied similar mice caught on the east coast and concluded that they were identical to an Egyptian subspecies, Mus musculus orientalis. As James Fairley put it charitably in his book A Basket of Weasels (2001), O'Mahony "had simply been carried away".

Prof Fairley also quoted an intriguing phenomenon cited by the naturalist Charles Moffat in the Irish Naturalists' Journal in 1929: "Most of us have, no doubt, been occasionally entertained by 'singing mice' and been struck with their tameness when pouring out their little melody – a melody often listened to, and rightly enough, with pathetic interest. It seems to be now beyond doubt that the song is an involuntary performance, due to some disease or derangement in the respiratory organs of the little singer." It's bad enough that our house mice move grand pianos around in the wall beside my bed. I don't want them singing along.

June 30th 2012

Irish badger, Mediterranean diet

It's a couple of years since, nipping out to measure the rain after breakfast, I met a badger in the garden, late on its way home. Halting in mid-step a couple of metres away, I had the honour of brief and thoughtful regard before it trundled off to the latest hole in the fence.

Such visits, regular in February, are otherwise evident from divots dug out of the lawn as the badger hunts for leatherjackets, the juicy grubs of crane flies. These dominate the diet of Irish badgers in spring.

Then it's frogs and the grub-filled nests of wasps and bumblebees, followed, as summer fades into autumn, by a leaner feast of moth caterpillars of the smooth, unhairy kind.

This menu of dominant seasonal foods of Ireland's Meles meles was gleaned from the stomachs of 656 badgers, assembled, presumably, from among those culled to control cross-infection of cattle with TB.

Removing, in some years, more than 7,000 badgers from targeted areas across the island, the programme has prompted, together with protest, a lot of research. Much of it shows up the differences between the lifestyles of badgers in Ireland and those in Britain.

Indeed, it now seems Ireland's badgers could be a very special breed.

In diet, the near absence of earthworms as bulk food is notable: they're eaten often but scantily compared with the big reliance on worms by badgers on English farmland. Other ecological differences are summed up in a new review led by Dr Andrew Byrne of Teagasc.

Smaller Irish badger groups excavate smaller main setts, often in hedgerows, while British badgers dig vast, labyrinthine setts among the root spread of trees.

Badgers move around more in Ireland, their social groups are more fluid and the female reproductive cycle seems to have differences in timing.

How many badgers we have has been steeply revised – and not by the losses through culling. An extrapolated estimate in 1995 put the Republic's population at 200,500. In 2009, with better information on badger movements, Dr Paddy Sleeman of University College Cork judged the total at 84,000 and the average size of badger group at only 3.9 compared with Britain's 5.9.

All this, however, has been outshone in significance by DNA research on the origins of Ireland's badgers.

When, in her study of badger diet, Dr Gráinne Cleary of Trinity College Dublin concluded that "this feeding behaviour is more similar to that of badgers in Italy and Spain than to badgers in England" she was touching on a deeper mystery.

In the prestigious Biological Journal of the Linnean Society is a paper on the genetic structure of European badgers and their colonisation of Ireland, the work of a twelve-strong team of Irish and American scientists led by Dr Denise O'Meara of University College Cork and Dr Ceiridwen Edwards of Trinity College Dublin. It shows that badgers in Britain could be subdivided into several populations, most of them genetically grouped with those of Central Europe. But Ireland has just one population that shares, with Scandinavia, genetic affinities with the badgers of Spain.

The study considers DNA clues to "an Atlantic fringe element" already found in Irish mammals, such as the pygmy shrew and pine marten. While the hair, grease and meat of badgers could have earned them a place in the boats of prospecting Neolithic Spaniards, the team could find no evidence for this. Securely dated evidence for badgers in Ireland is absent until medieval times, yet, perhaps remarkably, the team entertains the chance that badgers could have colonised Ireland naturally – this from land to the southwest, exposed in the Ice Age.

However it arrived, it seems the Irish badger could be unique in its inheritance.

Indeed, the paper recommends "that future bovine TB culls in Ireland should carefully consider the genetic repercussions to Ireland's unique fauna". It points to the differences in diet, behaviour and tuberculosis levels between Irish and British badgers that may be influenced by their genes.

All this comes at a crucial point in Ireland's bovine TB control, as the policy of badger culling in "hot spot" areas, begun in 1989, gives way to the committed use of vaccinating baits. Effective baits carrying a modified BCG vaccine have taken more than a decade to develop and test.

Field trials of their impact on about 300 badgers living in setts across 755 square kilometres of Co Kilkenny began in 2009 and are due to conclude this year.

The baits needed a flavour irresistible to badgers. Aniseed, apple, curry, fish, garlic, peanut and strawberry were all tested in the field. Carob and cocoa powder are the most eagerly gobbled up, as a chocolate-covered badger bar.

July 7th 2012
Up the hill before breakfast

The ridge above us is an undistinguished lump of a hill, a long claw of Mweel-rea Mountain about 300 metres high. There are great views from the top. A rich old man with a helicopter used to touch down there on his way to buy crab claws in Connemara. He'd stand for a while and look, and perhaps take a meditative pee.

Once, in training as a gooseherd for a Greenland expedition, I climbed the hill every morning before breakfast, my backpack heavy with rope for extra virtue. It was a slog up rushy, rocky pasture, then the mountain fence and the grassy, boggy scarp beyond. But at the crest – ah! – the world right around, from Croagh Patrick to the Bens, the islands from 'Bofin to Achill.

Where the ridge broadens out there are long-abandoned turf cuttings and little platforms of stone where the sods were dried in the wind. There would still have been heather on the hillside then, and even fraughans for a picnic at Lughnasa, on the last Sunday in July.

The Reek – Croagh Patrick – was just one location for this old Celtic fes-tival, ending the summer with thanks for the harvest. All over Ireland peo-ple were climbing hills for Fraughan Sunday, Garland Sunday, Mountain

Sunday, Domhnach Crom Dubh. And the fraughans were bilberries, blaeberries, whinberries, heatherberries, whorts or mónógs, all Vaccinium myrtillus, wild cousin of the big, cultivated blueberry, today's antioxidant elixir.

"Berry black, with blue bloom, sweet. Mountains, heaths and woods on acid soil, abundant." Thus a summary in the new edition of Webb's An Irish Flora. But the map in the New Atlas of the British & Irish Flora (2002) shows big blank areas for the bilberry in north Leinster and in parts of the west and midlands where the shrub grew before 1970.

Urban sprawl, conifer forestry and sheep overgrazing can be blamed.

"Seventy years after the last peak in exports to Britain in the 1940s," writes Dr Michael Conry, "it is now difficult to find enough bilberries to make a bit of jam or a bilberry pie." Conry, a retired soil scientist with An Foras Talúntais, had the friendship and encouragement of the late and great Prof Frank Mitchell. This inspired his explorations of rural culture and folkways and handsome, self-published books such as Culm Crushers, The Carlow Fence and Corn Stacks on Stilts.

His latest, Picking Bilberries, Fraocháns and Whorts in Ireland: The Human Story (conry-michael-books.com), is the most remarkable of all. A chronicle of Ireland's long affair with a bountiful wild fruit, it documents in great detail some striking but near-forgotten episodes of rural survival and enterprise. Interviews with "hundreds, if not thousands of people" all over Ireland, and old pictures from their family albums, tell the story.

Bilberry-eating goes back forever: the seeds survived for archaeology in the cesspits of Viking Dublin. But in the first and second World Wars, when prices soared for bilberry exports to Britain, whole townlands of families climbed to the high woods and hillsides of southeastern Ireland, day after day for six weeks and more, suffering thorny briars, midges, face flies, wasp nests and ticks to fill their buckets and baskets. ("Bottoming the can", we're told, was the crucial psychological breakthrough of a slow and tedious task.) Bought and cleaned by local dealers, the berries were shipped off within twenty-four hours – some 400 tons of them in 1941, an exceptionally good year (when British pilots, reportedly, found that bilberry jam improved their night vision). Bilberry money paid long-standing shop bills, provided dowries and bought bicycles, boots and schoolbooks.

Why the southeastern counties, in particular, should have met the wartime demand was not simply proximity to market. Bilberries grow best in well-drained acid soil beneath a canopy of broadleaf trees – Conry shows them growing in metre-high masses beneath maturing oak trees in Derrybawn Wood at Laragh, Co Wicklow. On old estates where the big trees had been felled they also survived well among heather, gorse and scrub oak; some land-lords, indeed, charged for access to the harvest.

A great many gaps in today's map of Ireland's bilberries correspond to the planting of conifer forest, whose dense shadow slowly overwhelmed the shrub. In my own locality this happened beside Louisburgh, where Kilgeever Hill, a pup to the Reek, now stands shorn of conifers and fraughans both. Bilberry pies and jam are still made in Ireland (not least by the neighbours of Mayo's Bilberry Lake, near Castlebar), but the hilltop festivities now belong to the land of Dev's comely maidens. In his 1950s classic, Irish Folk Ways, Estyn Evans could write that, while the fiddling and dancing of "Height Sunday" might have ceased on the summit of Co Down's Slieve Croob, "numbers of young people still assemble there and frolic in the heather". Today, one as-sumes, they stir no further than the back of the car.

August 11ᵗʰ 2012
Arachnophobia and appreciation

There was that scene in Great Expectations (we oldies saw the first film, in 1946) where Pip was summoned to Miss Havisham's room, where the wedding cake was slowly crumbling amid her broken dreams. Like everything else, it was shrouded in cobwebs, and, as Dickens wrote it, "speckle-legged spiders with blotchy bodies" ran around it on the tablecloth. I have edited those out of memory, but the room's veils of cobweb remain.

As the summer drizzles away, our spiders are dressing the house like a studio set. Their gauzy hammocks swing around the kitchen, blur corners of the living room, and drape the ceiling above the living room lights on the nights when we're having friends in.

We bought one of those yokes for vacuuming the car, initially for cleaning the books, but now also for sucking up as many webs as I can see. The spiders wait until I've finished, then creep out to start spinning again.

As a recovering arachnophobe, size matters.

In the loo, I can watch with equanimity as pale and fragile Pholcidae, their long legs scarcely pencilled in against the window, stalk midges in webs strung almost at random.

The webs that shroud window sill bric-a-brac – sea urchins, bird skulls, fossils from Aran – seem to belong to tiny spiders that follow their handiwork into the nozzle. I have left, for the moment, a dense funnel web in one corner, its depths strung with moth wings like scraps of Hermès scarves.

There's a dark hole at the bottom, drilled to admit the broadband aerial, and I fear it may house Tegenaria domestica, the barn spider that comes indoors.

This is the common horror that stalks abroad in autumn to pose on stark arenas of wall or ceiling, to be dashed at with kitchen towelling, smothered and flushed down the loo. There are people who "rescue" spiders with a tumbler and a piece of card, and deposit them tenderly in the garden, but I have yet to graduate to such proper regard. At least I no longer whinny and summon Ethna from her desk.

Autumn, on the other hand, can also conjure the spectacle I first encountered down at the swans' lake behind the shore, where vertical threads of spider silk shimmered above the water, a gauzy, sunlit curtain waving against the darkness of the cliff. And a reader once wrote to Eye on Nature about his surreally beautiful sight in Dublin's Phoenix Park, when "what I took to be the low winter sun reflecting off waterlogged ground turned out to be an infinity of strands of silk stretched across the grass as far as the eye could see. Close by, they shimmered in the sunlight like a moonlit sea, and as I watched I saw additional strands drift along over the ground until snagged on a blade of grass."

All this was gossamer, depositing thousands of diminutive, ballooning Linyphiid spiders ("money spiders" in childhood's litany of good-luck portents). Darwin found thousands of these little red spiders covering the rigging of HMS Beagle as it lay 100 kilometres off the coast of Argentina. On land, he also watched the behaviour described in my spider book (a Hamlyn one, packed with close-up photographs I cannot bear to consult).

A spider intent on ballooning climbs to a high point, such as the top of a fence, and turns to face into the wind. It extrudes several strands of silk and then, when the wind is strong enough to lift them, stands on tiptoe and lets go the grip of its little claws. It's not just adult Linyphiids that use this method of dispersal – other small adults and the young of many species go ballooning, often for great distances, as late as December. They have been caught at every altitude up to 4,500 metres, but most seem content to skim the highest trees.

Blowing in to Ireland on a silken strand was one way for spiders to colonise the island after the Ice Age. Working out which species arrived that way, and which might have been tucked into bird feathers or Neolithic currachs, which hitched a lift on driftwood, or crept back from some offshore refuge, awaits its turn for research.

September 22nd 2012
A good year for caterpillars

At rest it looks, for those who remember such things, rather like a small, dark cheroot, of the kind once – perhaps still – clamped between the shiny teeth of Mexican bandits. Close up, however, its skin has the sheen of a soft velour, patterned with moth colours like a 1920s sofa. And when alarmed, in a quite absurd simile of its own, it pulls in its snout and puffs up its eye spots to look as much like a menacing snake as a caterpillar can.

This autumn seems to be good for spotting the larva of Deilephila elpenor, the elephant hawkmoth, judging by the number of reader reports, some full of the awe of a first encounter. This is, indeed, one of Ireland's largest native caterpillars, growing up to seven centimetres, and much more often seen than the hawkmoth that begets it. That's a pity, as the moth is a beautiful arrowhead of bright pink and gold wings, seeking nectar in flowers by night and able to tell their colour even by starlight.

Not that the bright, long-tubed honeysuckle that fits the hawkmoth's tongue especially well would take much finding. But the really important plants of its life are chosen to feed its caterpillars, not itself, and neither rosebay willowherb nor fuchsia exactly shines in the dark. Soon after a ghostly midnight copulation, which can last up to two hours, the female starts laying her glossy green eggs, continuing for several nights until she has deposited about 100, one by one.

The bond that most butterflies and moths have with particular plants to feed their larval stage is part of the relationship between plants and insects that powered much of the diversity of the natural world. Buy a field guide to caterpillars (Collins does the standard one, by Carter and Hargreaves) and you find colour plates bright with the caterpillars that feed on particular groups of trees and plants.

The cabbage whites seem obvious, but the food plant index runs long, from alder to zea (maize), each with its own lepidopteral consumers.

Some species make a wide choice among quite separate groups of plants, but the bonds can be so exclusive that the very survival of a butterfly species depends on the existence of the plant and conservation of its habitat. In Ireland, for example, only the devil's bit scabious of wet grassland feeds the black caterpillars of the endangered marsh fritillary butterfly.

Such close affinities have encouraged the idea of co-evolution between these insects and their food plants, with some even proposing that butterflies and moths reached the peak of their development at the same time as the flowering plants. But study still goes on as to why, exactly, such partnerships were formed and still endure. Taken to America, Europe's cabbage whites insist on laying eggs on sulphurous European brassicas instead of switching to native species.

What is it about rosebay willowherb, for example, that so appeals to the elephant hawkmoth? This plant can sweep a lovely pink haze across a hillside of clear-felled forestry. I have admired it in the summer of the Greenland wilderness. It is the postinferno "fireweed" of Canada, and, having flourished on the bomb sites of London, it is now that city's county flower.

Is it the plant's chemistry, structure, nutritional quality or parasite-free space that makes it fit so well, and that makes fuchsia, an alien shrub in these islands, an acceptable alternative? (For some British gardeners, indeed, the caterpillars' appetite for fuchsia makes it a pest.) While blossoms themselves may play little part in the diet of caterpillars, it is the emergence of flowering plants (angiosperms) and their interaction with pollinating insects that has been credited with the great surge in the planet's insect biodiversity. But in 1995 came the apparent discovery, in a petrified forest in Arizona, of bees' nests and wasp cocoons fossilised into the trees and 100 million years older than fossil evidence for the earliest flowers, from some 140 million years ago.

Enough sober and prestigious American scientists were sufficiently impressed to put legs, so to speak, under the possibility that bees could have evolved before there was nectar in the world, or colourful petals to lead the insects in. Before the flowering angiosperms, the planet's vegetation was the lush greenery of the gymnosperms, mostly conifers and ferns.

Harvard's eminent Stephen Jay Gould, always ready for a scientific challenge, was quite open to the possibility that early bees were already pollinating gymnosperms. The angiosperms, perhaps, developed new ways of attracting their visits.

By 2006, a rival camp of palaeontologists had inspected the Arizona fossil cells and declared them more likely to have been left by some Triassic beetle-like creature.

In any case, Dr Stephen Hasiotis, their discoverer, continues to lecture at the University of Kansas. One of his geology students describes him as wearing "a fanny pack, skin-tight jeans, a Hawaiian shirt and boots every day" and being "fairly funny". None of that, of course, makes him wrong.

September 29th 2012
Magnificent autumn moons

A different lift to the wind, a new slant to the sky: as autumn unfolds, the west comes into its own. Like the great spring tides that surge across the strand, wiping it clean as a mirror, a realignment of light and space creates a bright new stage for the landscape, suddenly colourful in ways the summer people never see.

Summer's high, flat light is as bland and clumsy as a passport photograph, if not attenuated by mist or drizzle, then soaked up by grasses in their beige shroud of high-season pollen. An October sun is a portraitist, a sculptor, glittering in the spikes of morning rushes, the cobwebs of hedges and lichened walls.

The mountains are given back their drama, sharp-edged and shadowed, reunited with their past, their glacial shaping lovingly detailed, the last erratic boulder spotlit in the bog. A moorland suffused with the death of sedges – madders and crimsons – sets its own fires from the torch of the sun: the smouldering siennas of falling bracken, the lion's mane flare of moorgrass, bleached late into winter. It's then that the little lakes shine bluest, like shards of lapis lazuli or cobalt.

For the moment, though, let's settle for the autumn's magnificent moons: the harvest moon tomorrow night, when the final two per cent of the orb becomes visible, cloud permitting, in Ireland, and the full hunter's moon of October.

They must, of course, be shared with lesser skies (did I never notice them in Dublin, even on starstruck party nights?), but here they rise, already golden and enormous, from the ridge above Six Noggins. They sparkle for a while in the hill stream at the bridge, then lift above the peak of Mweelrea to make a silver ribbon of the boreen to the sea. If I am lucky, early at my desk, one still towers above the islands, mocking the earthbound scan of my computer.

Both moons invite what is termed the moon illusion: the conviction of so many people that full moons look biggest of all soon after clearing the horizon. Science admits the illusion but still can't quite account for it.

Ptolemy's notion is still current: that the low moon looks bigger because we have foreground objects against which to measure it. The rich colour of the low moon, warmed to marzipan by industrial haze, may play a part too.

In 1709, George Berkeley, Irish bishop and philosopher, isolated the rising moon by looking at it through a tube, but he found that it still looked bigger.

Patrick Moore, the moon's ambassador on Earth, once stood on his head on the shore at Selsey Bill to see if that made any difference.

It didn't.

I have wondered, if the moon rose in the west, in the pristine air of the Atlantic, would the moon illusion fade? Mayo's fabulous sunsets, after all, often most brilliant in November, owe nothing to dust or haze for their incandescent colours. If that were true, as one American weatherman has pointed out, "cities such as New York, Los Angeles, London and Mexico City would be celebrated for their twilight hues." Stephen F Corfidi is lead forecaster for the National Oceanic and Atmospheric Administration storm-prediction centre (noaa.gov), a great source of meteorological enlightenment. Late autumn and winter produce eastern America's best sunsets, too, most memorably, as here at Thallabawn, when the right kind of clouds enrich and reflect a low but unadulterated sunlight.

The blazing reds and oranges are what remain of the visible spectrum when the beam from a low setting sun has been robbed of the violet and blue light that illumine our perception of the daytime sky. The purer the air, the more its molecules scatter the violet wavelengths; droplets of haze or pollution merely dull or subdue the colours, robbing the sunset of brilliance and intensity. That the west's Atlantic sunsets of late autumn are so vivid, often suffusing even the lowest clouds, is evidence of clean air, right down to the swells of the ocean.

All this, and I have not even spoken of the stars. On those night photographs of Earth from space, the coast of Connacht is one of the last, blessedly dark fringes of Europe. The overpowering awe of a clear starry sky is another spectacular offering of the west; some city dwellers, indeed, on their first revelation, stand transfixed with jaws ajar, adrift in the infinite Milky Way.

Great moons, spectacular sunsets, starry skies, a landscape transformed by the angle of the sun: how real is all this, how probable, how bookable in advance? Will the websites of country house hotels offer last-minute deals to match a promising weather forecast? Or have I, from decades in the west, woven an off-season idyll from too many singular visions?

October 13th 2012

A new Ice Age theory

The Inuit word nunataq has always appealed to me – an evocative, spiky sound. Geology borrowed it from Greenland to describe peaks of mountains that stick up through the ice. In Ireland's big glaciations, heaped hugely over the north, some summits stayed ice free. They poked up in the Wicklows, the Knockmealdowns and the Galtees and in Connemara. Our mountain, Mweelrea, was also a nunatak – the anglicised spelling changes the Inuit slightly – leaving frost-shattered rock at the summit to clatter under one's boots.

Nunataks were far too small to sustain the few native species that lived through the last of the ice. The Irish stoat and the Irish hare certainly were not sharing the same mountaintops. So where were they? Study of the Quaternary period, as it's called, has focused on the last two big glaciations, the Munsterian and the Midlandian. In the Munsterian Cold Stage, most of the island seems to have been buried at some stage, right to the south coast and beyond.

In the later Midlandian Cold Stage, beginning about 80,000 years ago, a great oval ice cap was pictured reaching across to a line of moraines from the Shannon to Wicklow, with an isolated ice cap on the Cork and Kerry Mountains and dry tundra left across most of Munster.

With the level of the sea having fallen by up to 120 metres, its water gone to make ice, there were also great reaches of exposed seabed. Some Irish scientists thought this offshore land could have sheltered some plants and wildlife, but most argued about possible land bridges from Britain, supplying Ireland with wildlife as the ice retreated.

In the late twentieth century the whole Midlandian picture was changed. Dr William Warren of the Geological Survey of Ireland proposed three major ice domes on Ireland, merging with the Irish Sea ice lobe to cover the island completely. Research has since been confirming his ideas. A key study by Prof Colm Ó Cofaigh and his team has the last ice covering most of Munster, with the midland moraines created in the retreat, not the advance, of the glaciers.

An important contribution on the spread of the ice has come from the quaternary environmental change research group at the University of Ulster at Coleraine, led by Dr Paul Dunlop. It used the maps of the Irish National Seabed Survey to trace the edge of it through seabed marks and gravel ridges.

These showed land-bound ice extending westwards beyond the island for ninety kilometres or more, in places reaching the great precipice of the Atlantic continental shelf.

The shelf continues off the southwest of Ireland, curving back into the Bay of Biscay, its undersea cliff edge steep and scored by great canyons and meandering "riverbeds" carved by the westward rush of sediments.

But most of the shallower Celtic Sea fell outside the great wedge of Ireland's seabed domain. How far south of the Munster coast the final glaciers reached is thus still deeply mysterious, though, farther east, ice seems to have crept south of the Isles of Scilly.

To the west of Ireland its edge met Atlantic waves. These followed it in as it retreated, leaving no room for any wildlife refuge.

But the shelf to the south, towards Spain, may be more accommodating. Arguments on land bridges to Britain are becoming redundant as genetic research links more and more Irish species to Iberia and Europe. The idea of some midway southern ecosystem, sheltering animals and plants through the last of the Ice Age, has been reborn.

In an emergent new grouping of "native" Irish species, some with ancient and very unusual DNA profiles, the animal list runs as follows: Irish stoat, hare, otter, badger, red squirrel, wood mouse, Leisler's bat, natterjack toad and frog, not to mention the hairy wood ant, Formica lugubris, driven to inbreeding in its lonely forest mounds. Even Connemara's "Lusitanian" heather species, St Dabeoc's heath, seems to have spent time in a refuge somewhere now drowned in the Bay of Biscay.

Indeed, as Dr Jim Provan of Queen's University Belfast allows: "We cannot conclusively rule out the existence of a small, more northerly refugium." If all the species listed above were living somewhere together, theirs would have been an elaborate Arcadia, demanding, as the University College Cork zoologist Dr Paddy Sleeman admits, a coastal location with woods and fresh water. In all the shallow ocean explored for the National Seabed Survey, the scratches of grounded icebergs appear everywhere. And could a wooded "refuge" zone have retreated and advanced with the spread and withdrawal of ice? For the moment its existence can seem as conjectural as that of Hy Brasil. But genetic research seems to have sunk the once-inevitable bridges to Britain, and southern reaches of the Celtic Sea could hold more big surprises.

November 10ᵗʰ 2012

The last of the ash trees?

The demise of the tree would be a terrible blow to what is left of our native landscape. The ash tree outside the living room window is down to its last few fronds, the bare branches smooth and silvery against the coppery glow of a young beech beyond.

It's twenty-two years this month since we lifted the ash seedling from a forest path at Cong. We planted it, of course, too close to the house. In full flush it shades the lean-to greenhouse and has us peering out into the leaves, a thrilling lettuce-green in spring, thereafter cool as an aquarium, with flashes of blackbird and thrush.

Inland ashes sometimes keep their leaves for a brief autumn ignition of lime and saffron, flaring against a slanting sun. But ours is the last of our trees to burst into leaf and first to unlatch them in October.

Thus it dodges most of the salty storms that might blunt its lovely winter shape, a bare but billowy candelabra gilded in every ocean sunset.

Twenty-two years is nothing in the life of Fraxinus excelsior, even as dark moss tucks into its armpits and gold and green lichens wrap around its bark. Two to three centuries is more like it, especially when coppicing teases the sap to rise forever. But now, of course, we have to wonder if, here at a last slope of Europe, our acre will cherish one of the last trees of its kind, a few decades after we have gone.

Is that too much hyperbole? In Britain, as I write, the threat to that island's eighty million ash trees is already considered beyond confinement. The killing fungus Chalara fraxinea was imported in ash saplings from a mainland Europe already ravaged by the disease.

But beyond all the tainted nurseries and plantations are dozens of wild woodlands now found with chalara. Most are clustered around Britain's southeastern littoral and all too probably infected by spores of the fungus blown across from continental shores a mere ferry ride away. In Ireland, too, the first casualties are among ash saplings imported from the Netherlands.

Having put a stop to that, and then destroyed the trees in a wide scatter of plantations, the latest bans prohibit ash boles with their bark on, brought in for hurley manufacture, and raw timber for firewood and pellet stoves. As practical action it's about the best we can do.

Unfortunately, short of some miraculously curative spray, the westward drift of this new natural plague, an apparent fungal mutation, seems every bit as inevitable as the march of Dutch elm disease in the later twentieth century.

A recent New Scientist found feelings of futility in even the most knowledgeable of European experts. If the trees are chopped down, "the infective material is all on the forest floor and cannot be removed or eradicated with fungicides without destroying countless other forms of forest life."

In Ireland, ash is the typical hedgerow tree, often burdened in winter with dark shrouds of ivy that would not be found (or, perhaps, tolerated) in mainland Europe. However valued ivy may be for wildlife, its wind-catching canopy bulk puts trees at risk in storms, so that wild roadside ashes with the stag's head silhouette of dieback would invite the earliest destruction.

Ash and ivy are also partnered in the botanical name of one of Ireland's most characteristic types of native woodland, Fraxinus excelsior-Hedera helix. On the relatively dry and lime-rich lowlands of the midlands and east, ash-ivy woods (perhaps with a scattering of pedunculate oaks and birch, beech and sycamore) are the island's richest habitat for colourful spring flowers. The ash's late budburst lets in the sunlight to primroses, anemones and bluebells, violets, celandines and orchids.

This gift of early light to the forest floor is perhaps the ash's outstanding ecological virtue. Lacking crevices and dense foliage, it hosts a fraction of the plant-eating insects and mites attracted to the pedunculate oak (about forty, compared with the oak's 284) and offers too little cover and food for nesting birds. One ash at moist Killarney hosts more than forty kinds of lichen, but the oak, again, tops 300.

In its 4,000 years on the island the fuinseog has had most value, perhaps, for people; certainly, we should miss it terribly from what is left of the native landscape.

The giant ashes of earlier centuries have entirely disappeared, among them the massive one at Emo, Co Laois, its main stem measured at twenty-five feet round in 1792.

Sacred and curative ashes have haunted Irish folklore, inspiring whole books to list them. Trees hung with rags above holy wells or hammered with coins until they died of a thousand offerings; ash trees as proxy for saints or for funerals to walk around on the way to the grave.

One of these "funerary trees", growing near Cong, ended with a whole cairn of little stones tossed in around its base. Our own glows with life – we trust, a long one.

December 1st 2012
Walks on the wild side

To give the sights and sounds of the hillside their proper attention, you must go unplugged. Sometimes at weekends, when RTÉ fills the early morning with pop music that does not engage me (pretty well all of it since the Bee Gees and The Beatles), I leave earphones and MP3 behind on the half-hour march for my heart's ease.

Briskly downhill to the last farm before the shore, up again more slowly with a couple of pauses for reflection, and my attention is restored to the sounds and sights of the hillside.

There must be people with earphones whose morning chore is three times around the Parthenon, dodging all the stone blocks the builders have left lying around, or a kilometre or two of the Grand Canyon, wishing they'd put in decent steps.

Familiarity breeds not exactly contempt but a readiness, let's say, to disengage.

Thus, without urgent affairs of state to grip my mind, I can appreciate the fuller experience of Thallabawn. This must include mornings when I head out into gale or rain, zipped and Velcroed to the eyeballs. The recommended five days a week doesn't work on the Atlantic coast: it's up to gale force eight or nothing. At least it's the cleanest wind and purest rain in Europe. And I am not alone.

As if timed to the minute for the same spot, I meet an approaching high-vis neighbour, halfway around a circuit twice the length of my own.

"Not nice!" we empathise, in a passing swish of lemon jackets.

With any luck, however, even in the current squeeze of autumn isobars, there is enough pause between showers and hail squalls for me to do The Grand Old Duke of York on our hill all unanoraked. I judge it by the distant sweep of curtains along the sea's horizon and the speed of their grey advance across 'Bofin or 'Turk.

The size of the rain pools on the road is another gauge of my chances.

A heron stood there the other morning, peering hopefully into ankle-deep water, perhaps for a wandering frog.

Such amazements are few. Old friends are the hares, crossing the boreen between regular notches worn in the field banks at either side.

With Meg no longer sniffing ahead, they can safely pause in the middle, at the Mohican stripe of grass, to appraise me with a huge sideways eye.

I remember the boreen before tarmacadam: stones all the way to the sea. Where curling bracken waves now in its last, lacy fronds of beige and russet, the winter verges were mown by loose cattle set free to graze the "long acre".

The few cattle left on the hillside today are well-fed captives, with yellow tags in their ears, and it's sheep that climb field banks to strain their necks through the fence for the extra bite. Sometimes, panicking at my step, they get their horns tangled as they jerk back: I worry they will hang there, strangling, and sometimes stop for them to take their time.

The verges are thick with herbs and grasses, combed one way by the wind from the sea, and I note the empty glove of a hedgehog on the tar, its spines a bit flatter every day. Adding it to the records at biology.ie, it is the 697th dead hedgehog sighted on the roads this year.

Sounds of the hillside blur wind and surf, and the rattle of streams as they foam through their clefts in the fields. Blackbirds squeal at me from hedges; jackdaws erupt, barking, from the guest-house shelter belt.

The young cock pheasant is still calling at the wrong season, forlornly far off in the rushes. And on calmer days, when the wind is right, descants of gossip float up from the shore, as whooper swans switch lagoons.

Out there, beyond the channel and the dunes, waits the wild side of Thallabawn, where otters run up from the sea with fish and something new – who knows what? – waits at the edge of the tide.

In the early years, I could not pass any of the big Atlantic trawler balls without hoisting the best across my shoulder: stacked up on ropes at the woodshed, they bring bright winter colour to the garden. Lovely, like the green glass net balls of a previous technology, they seem to be washed up far more rarely now.

But how would I know, really? Search effort heads the equation in beach-combing discoveries, or my window sills would not be so littered with curious bits and pieces, shells, bones, skulls and beans. These are all from the years of an almost daily patrol of the tideline, and what's rare is still largely a matter of who's around to see.

For the moment, and possibly longer, the morning march before breakfast will suffice, with occasional forays beyond: some, indeed, to keep the sanderling company right at the edge of the ocean. Even the march down the hill has its memories; a heron fishing in a puddle isn't bad.

And there's always – well, quite often – the view.

December 8th 2012
My Irish Times debut

The flight of birds across the hillside is now sparse but more eventful, as the local finches and starlings sift about in flocks, the better to find food and keep a heads-up for predators. Among them, I assume, are the goldfinches we gloried in all summer as they raised young on the acre. As late as September, one cock was still uttering his delicious, swivelling song from the hawthorn.

When the wind went north last month we took out the feeders and opened the big bag of peanuts from Argentina. Days on, as I write, the tubes hang almost untouched from the oaks: even the garden tits must feel they have wild seeds enough. But goldfinches will be back as the last of the wayside thistles are scalped, until perhaps a dozen are flashing about the trees.

I remember the great pleasure, more than a decade ago, when the first of these finches came to the nuts – a thrill shared at thousands of Ireland's kitchen windows as a species most at home in a weedy countryside progressively discovered human bounty. There have even been queries to Eye on Nature from innocents dazzled by the brilliant colours: what exotic visitors could they be?

The great change in the bird's fortunes can be judged from its profile in an early classic of Irish ornithology, Birds of Ireland, published in 1900. "The goldfinch," Richard Ussher and Robert Warren began, "is a well-known bird in every part of Ireland from which bird-catchers have not driven it, though they have done this for miles around our larger towns and even in many country districts the species has sensibly diminished."

The popularity of captive goldfinches as caged birds, many for export to the UK, persisted for decades. In 1930, a young Dáil deputy for Dublin South, Mr Seán Lemass, was resisting the passage of the first Protection of Wild Birds Act. It would, he said, bring greater misery to the 300 people who made a precarious living from the birdcatching trade. "If the economic situation becomes better," he went on, "we can then afford to indulge in luxury legislation of this kind..."

At the end of the 1950s, on a brief visit to Ireland, I was taken around Dublin by a friend. The tour included a Sunday morning visit to the old bird market in what was once called Petty Canon Alley, later Canon Street, within bell-ringing chimes of St Patrick's Cathedral. This cramped little cul-de-sac was lined with cages around the walls holding, all too probably, some goldfinches and linnets along with canaries and budgerigars. The alley was crowded with men in hats and caps who, in retrospective fancy, could have been waiting to join Flann O'Brien in the pub.

The visit moved me to a poem, some of which went as follows: "There would be something doubly wrong / About a market selling birds in cages / That kept a view of distant hills, / Of songbirds free to leafy refuges. / This market is itself a cell confined by overpeering walls…" And so on. I was twentysomething, and The Irish Times kindly paid me a tenner for it – my debut in these pages.

December 22nd 2012
Goodbye to the goose

Keeping poultry is lovely in theory, but in practice it is a full commitment with a deathly ring. To kill your goose for Christmas, the "alternative" books said, lower it so that its beak stretches along the ground, set a broomstick across the back of its neck, put a foot on either end, and then…I won't go on, not least because it didn't always work as it should, leaving me with some quite traumatic memories.

Later, we took to buying a goose from a farmer's wife along the hill.

She delivered it trussed but alive, killing being a man's job. Even switching to a hatchet, while mercifully quicker (for me, at least), there was nothing remotely merry about a self-sufficient executioner. Today we eat guinea fowl, conjured from the everyday world that conducts its slaughter by proxy.

Ethna's mother had a little poultry farm at the foot of Cuilcagh Mountain in Cavan. She kept a licensed turkey cock when all these birds were bronze and very beautiful, with dark but iridescent plumage. They could also mate naturally, a gift now lost to turkeys bred by insemination to provide billowing breasts of whiter, less gamey, meat. Bronze turkeys are now "heritage" birds, prerogative of the organic, greener and premium-rich side of society.

The Cavan family heritage encouraged our early ventures into keeping poultry: hens, geese and ducks, mainly for their eggs. Ethna, however, armed with powerful childhood recollections, made one proviso: man not only killed things, he also cleaned out the henhouse.

Constructing an intricate henhouse of cedar and marine ply was the next best delight to boatbuilding. (Some, after all, are deservedly called arks.) Collecting warm, fresh eggs from beneath the fluffy bums was one of life's great pleasures. Scraping off the droppings board each week was not.

Geese release their droppings as they go – a fresh, green cheroot of half-digested grass every few minutes – and this, in the end, brought our experiment to an end, as geese kept on inadequate stretches of grass do not stay healthy. We were sorry to see them go and so, I choose to think, was the little dairy goat we called Nancy.

The geese, ducks and goats (for milk) all spent much of their time in the big green hollow carved out by the hill stream, a sociable space now quite eclipsed by thickets of rampant fuchsia. The relationship between Nancy and one of the geese was somewhat hard to judge. I came upon them as the goat was tugging with her teeth at the goose's white breast feathers, pulling the bird this way and that. But far from moving away (the bird was free to retreat, while the goat was on a tether to a concrete block), she seemed not to mind it at all. Released, she stood where she was and it was Nancy who desisted.

On subsequent days it became clear that the goose liked what was happening, hanging around beside Nancy until she pulled at her feathers again. Indeed, I was there when she succeeded in plucking a good mouthful – no easy task – and chewed and swallowed them, while the goose looked on, unperturbed.

As for the ducks – lovely, jolly, noisy Aylesburys, their white wings silky as bombazine – their essentially unruly nature undid them.

Enjoying the stream no end on long summer days, they would follow it under the bridge and up the hill, refusing to come home until the sun had set. One laid its eggs among rushes on the bank for a hedgehog to raid in the night, and there were certainly other nests we never knew about.

Alert, finally, to their ways, an otter picked them off one by one, just as their successors, as chicks in a pen, succumbed to a stoat.

Two generations of hens, too, fell to a violent fate, the first from a roaming dog, the next to a fox that ferried their corpses up the hill and cached them in its den.

Such serial predation became wearing, especially as each affair seemed to seek out some failing of our own. (The fox came at dusk, when Christmas entertaining made us forget to close the hens in.) But honesty compels further reasons why the henhouse now decays, like a crumbling dacha, in the shadows of our densest spinney, and the duck house has vanished in the fuchsia.

Keeping livestock of any sort means constant commitment – no nipping off to make films, which happened to be our late vocation. I mention this now as it's in the quiet and well-fed days after Christmas that self-sufficient aspirations are likely to take hold at the fireside. Yes, it would be a lot of fun, besides saving money, and there are shelves of good books about how to do anything you've a mind to. But when the ducks come quacking outside the kitchen window, they expect you to be there.

January 19th 2013
The rewilding of Ireland

At what better time in the past, I have wondered, would my Mayo hillside have been more "natural"? And, then, more natural in what way? Without going back to the start, as it were, to Jurassic dragons in fern forests, where to begin? Not, certainly, within cultural memory, as conjured by tumbled gables and grassed-over lazy beds.

In that time, with most of eight and a half million people in the countryside, the hillside was black, under intense cultivation: potatoes and oats in summer, weeds in winter. On the hilltop, cattle in the heather; on the shore, much carting of seaweed and shell sand. Turf mined anywhere within donkey distance and cut right down to the stones. Inland, outside of the big-house estates, hedgerows stripped of anything burnable.

Before that, and the western irruption of people, our corner of Connacht was, indeed, pretty wild, though the old maps came up with a scatter of early townland names. Shreds of old vegetation linger in difficult folds of the land: oaks crouched under cliffs; hazels dwarfed along the boreen to the sea. Pine roots carved from the bog, raw and red as butcher's bones, speak of ancient, native forest but also of climate change as the postglacial ocean rose and the smothering mosses swelled up with rain. Somewhere between, the landscape found room for eagles and last wolves, along with a sprinkle of people.

Within Europe, visions of "natural" landscape aspire to a grander scale. As rural populations wither and marginal land falls back to scrub, the Rewilding Europe movement (rewildingeurope.com) urges its designs on areas as big as Ireland. Western Iberia, the Polish Carpathians, Croatian mountains (still scattered with landmines), all are offered a future as managed wilderness, part for biodiversity, part for human society. Natural grazing by wild horses, bison, elk and deer would cut the risk of bush fires; hunters would have more to shoot; tourists with binoculars would flock to B&Bs on former farmland.

The scale can be smaller. In the Scottish highlands, at Alladale, a posh hotel promotes a wilderness reserve, well furnished with indigenous pines but now boasting elk, red deer, ospreys and eagles in the course of "ecological restoration". This is now a buzz term in conservation management, but it raises the questions I began with. Restoration to what nature and when? As most of our mammals were imported by human people at various postglacial times, some fine judgments would be needed before adding any one of them to the view.

Even birds, it seems, can be asked for their passports. At Christmas, I reviewed a new bird book by Anthony McGeehan, Birds Through Irish Eyes (Collins Press), that challenged as "unethical" the release of red kites in Co Down – a species the author strongly suspects "was never here".

Gordon D'Arcy's earlier book, Ireland's Lost Birds (Four Courts, 1999), seemed to allow that kites might have roamed north from Leinster.

But McGeehan was really raising a bigger argument. How many reintroductions – of charismatic birds of prey, for example – appeal more to human pleasure (and thus the human purse and support) than improving the natural world for its own inherent value? Get existing habitats right, he urges, and pioneering wanderers will find them – or not, as nature decides.

He cites rediscovery of Leinster woods by the great spotted woodpecker and the new spread of buzzards across a more tolerant countryside.

Ireland has virtually no wild habitats, except the strip between the tides (and not always then). Most of the nature we know is a human construct, both in what we've added over centuries and – much more often – what we've taken away. Even the kind of natural world we might prefer is put together from Victorian books and paintings. The line between ecological repair and much-derided "wildlife gardening" can be lost in a confusion of science and human aesthetics.

At Ireland's size, we have no room for rewilding: there are far too many deer already, and a few introduced wild boar are now hunted as an "invasive alien species".

Conservationists can argue that bringing back kites and eagles helps to turn people on to nature, respecting and preserving the homes of lesser creatures as well as filling B&Bs. It heals a few scars from our game-keepered past while ignoring, too often, the modern rise of predators – mink, rats, foxes, grey crows – that are wrecking the landscape's natural inheritance of species.

Red kites, meanwhile, once the specialist scavengers of every European city, have been paying a high price for their reintroduction to the northern fringes of Dublin.

Following the success of introducing kites from Wales to Wicklow, beginning in 2007, 39 young birds were released in Fingal in 2011 and quickly spread out between the coastal estuaries and Meath. By the end of their first winter, nine of them were dead, most poisoned by rodenticide in rats they had scavenged.

January 26th 2013

On the trail of an otter

It's an age since I actually saw an otter. On sorties to the strand, somewhat rarer now, I check a tuft of grass at the freshwater pool where a stream runs out to the channel. Green and lush from repeated doses of nitrogen, it bears the remains of the latest spraint, the otter's dropping; a tarry morsel with a musky, not displeasing scent.

And then, walking the tideline, I watch for the track of an otter, bringing its fish – small and flat, mostly, from these sandy shallows – across the dunes to chew among the marram. Or else, where the strand meets a rocky headland, tracks where an otter cuts up through a cleft in the dunes to a little marshy lake, there to rinse the sea salt from its fur.

There have been grand encounters, each good for a column or a marvellous minute of film: otter besieged by a raven for its fish; otter skipping past Michael Longley's shins as he paddled in an autumn surf; otter ascending the highest dune to pause at the frozen shadows of the Vineys and their dog. Now I rest content with the occasional trail of prints – the slanted arc

183

of toes around the pad as precise and distinctive as a potter's mark.

Otters hold so much of the essence of the wild, or as much as this island can boast. Where there are otters, water is clean, fish can flourish, banks have proper holes to rest in, people largely mind their own business – all's reasonably right with the natural world.

February 16ᵗʰ 2013

Ireland's 165 million frogs

It was my eightieth year to heaven, and I walked abroad in a promised sunny spell, the surf on the shore calmed down at last, to see if the frogs had remembered my birthday. They got it spot on in 1997 ("garden pond full of frogs and first spawn laid") and again in 2005, but since then I have lost the great gatherings that February used to bring of 100 or more shiny heads, knotted in rapt amplexus, pumping out mounds of jellied eggs to glisten in the sun.

The fault is all mine, as I let what remained of open water succumb to creeping grasses, toppling rushes, fallen leaves, in the pond's clear haste to become a fen.

Hauling out this matted biomass every autumn is now beyond me, so that, at the imminence of spring, the algal scents said to summon frogs to their mating pools must be quite overwhelmed. I suspect also that the last few loyal habitues have been hoovered up by the badger that visits us on tour in February, testing his weight on the pond's strawy mattress.

I do not, it turns out, need to feel at all guilty about depriving Rana temporaria of its breeding habitat. The Republic, at a new and highly rigorous calculation for the National Parks and Wildlife Service, has about 165 million frogs, happily mating almost anywhere there's water, and above all in the drainage ditches that edge the nation's fields. They are probably the island's most abundant vertebrate, next to the long-tailed field mouse.

This new and cheering estimate replaces the apprehension favoured a few years ago, as frog populations in many parts of the world were seen to suffer huge decline from fungal and viral diseases as well as a progressive loss of habitat.

Although no disease had reached Ireland, the steady obliteration of farm ponds and the sprawl of suburban development seemed likely to support the anecdotal reports of local scarcities. Despite two sampling surveys that seemed to find frogs where they should be, the NPWS reported an "unfavourable" conservation status for this protected species.

Proof for this, however, was clearly limited, and a first national survey was designed with all the bells, whistles and arithmetic of the latest population algorithms. (Aspiring young scientists may care to download the frog report from the NPWS website to see the sort of test they could be in for.) The fieldwork, too, most of it carried out by the nationwide network of NPWS wildlife wardens, was rigorous enough to need special training.

It was based on a simple truth – where there's frogspawn, there's frogs – but making sure of comparable inspections on squares of land and water truly representative of the current surface of the Republic needed a sampling programme of some complexity. Since the turn of the nineteenth century, for example, the numbers of farmland ponds had halved, especially in eastern cereal-growing counties like Wexford, but about two per cent of the Republic was still good frog-breeding habitat, ranging from lakes and canals to dune slacks and roadside ditches. Everything needed sampling, to a scientific plan.

Two springs ago, on 171 selected bits of the map 500 metres square, 405 water bodies were surveyed for spawn, with three return visits to check on frog numbers and accumulating spawn. Everything was carefully estimated, including dimensions and depth of the water. There was spawn in half the water bodies and three-quarters of the survey squares, with the greatest occurrence in Mayo, Sligo and Donegal.

Most obviously, the frogs of Ireland have adapted to the loss of ponds by moving to the ditches that drain our grassy fields: eighty-six per cent of them, no less, were breeding in these habitats (even in the west, where, confusingly, "ditches" are the banks above them, and the dug-out bits are the "drains") and fewer than five per cent were in farmland ponds.

This is not exactly a novel discovery: the concentration of Irish frogs in ditches and at the sides of streams in bogs was noted by scientists three decades ago. Intensive study of the species has extended even to the variable number of a tadpole's teeth. But the new survey makes Ireland one of the few countries with a robust headcount of Europe's common frog.

With an average of about two dozen per hectare, we come nowhere near Finland's teeming densities (up to eighty per hectare) or even those of good habitats in Scotland. But it's a healthy population, even sometimes "explosive" in breeding compared with the frogs of continental Europe. (A figure of 1,000 eggs per clump of spawn spans, like all averages, some wide extremes.)

Frogs control slugs and midge larvae. The adults help feed our otters, badgers herons and kestrels. The tadpoles feed dragonfly larvae and great diving beetles – and goldfish.

Which is why, if you have fish in your pond, you won't get any frogs.

March 2nd 2013

My special oasis

The tunnel could look a bit ugly anywhere else: you might not want it in the neighbour's garden, or even your own. But nestled discreetly in our sheltering tangle of trees it can even have flashes of beauty, as when a full moon lights mysterious fairy candles along its canopy or a setting sun glows silkily in folds of polythene.

Just now the plastic is misted on both sides with winter algae, which, along with overhanging branches, defeats the optimal spread of light. As I scrub off the green film with a window-cleaning yoke, I ponder those black splashes on the plastic beneath the sycamore. That must, I conclude in a rare eureka moment, be summer aphids sucking at the tree and dripping surplus, sugary honeydew from their rear ends.

Without clouds of wasps or butterflies to lap it all up, it made a perfect substrate for the growth of sooty mould.

Such interests add to one's pleasure in the special ecosystem of the polytunnel but scarcely matter to its main role for an oldie, which is as sanctuary, kingdom and passport out of time, never mind extending the seasons or even working on when hail showers are rattling off the roof. What matters in this arching envelope of luminosity is the perennial, ageless redemption of making things grow again.

With a canvas chair in which to pause from measured stoopings and kneelings, a radio wedged high in the rigging in the one perch that gets Lyric properly, a mobile in my pocket for spousely summons or comfort, this is my special oasis on the planet.

"Good morning, tunnel!" I cry foolishly, heaving back the door. (Prince Charles is not alone in talking to his plants.) What's there at the moment? Broad beans budding into flower, mangetout peas halfway up, a sudden swelling of overwintered cauliflowers. Salad stuff, of course, and young beetroot, spinach and chard; the first bright spears of garlic. Early potatoes bide their time in a bed dressed with compost from the worm bin and wood ash from the stove. Up in the house, on a warm window sill, three kinds of tomatoes push up their first leaves; peppers and aubergines, too.

Darwin would have loved a tunnel. He did build himself a greenhouse, but his mysterious tummy troubles meant that some of his most momentous experiments with plants had to take place in his study.

He found answers to just the same questions that grab us still. Young pea plants reach out their tendrils to coil around wire netting – but how did they know it was there? And how do their stem cells engineer that tight, spiralling grip? "I have had a sudden access of furor about climbers," Darwin wrote to his friend Joseph Hooker in 1864, and in no time, helped by his son Frank, his sick couch was surrounded by climbing plants in pots: runner beans, wild cucumbers, nasturtiums, clematis and dozens more.

Tropical house plants and vines filled every surface and shelf. As hops spiralled up their sticks, he tied weights to their tips to try to slow them down. Vines became covered with paint marks as he timed their twisting movements.

Plants, as they grow, respond to many forces at once: the pull of light and warmth, the push of wind, the weight of gravity. But what Darwin discovered was the spiralling, oscillating movement he called "circumnutation" (Latin for circle or sway). This is a waving around at the tip, in repeating circles or elipses, that is common to all plants as they grow. It is part of keeping their balance but also, in climbers, a search for support. (A bean shoot may circle in a radius of up to ten centimetres.) Plants vary in this movement and the time they take to gyrate: tulips take four hours, wheat about two. Darwin painstakingly monitored more than 300 species and found circumnutation in all, even plotting it on sheets of glass suspended horizontally above them. But his hypothesis that the spur to spin is inherent in all plants became challenged by those who thought gravity alone was the power at work.

Dr Daniel Chamovitz of Israel, discussing plant senses in What a Plant Knows (Oneworld, 2012), tells how seeds of Arabidopsis (the standard weedy plant of botanical experiment), germinating in the near weightless International Space Station, showed little spiral movements as they grew. Put on a centrifuge, however, their circlings became much more pronounced, as gravity became a necessary partner in the dance.

As for that grip on the stick, it's the first touch that counts. As the tendril brushes the support, the cells immediately in contact stop growing, while those on the opposite side continue to elongate, pushing the tendril around into a spiral. For our ordinary peas and beans, this, too, can take hours – too long, perhaps, to keep watching, even in your polytunnel chair.

April 6th 2013
The nature of the pope

Who suggested that God seems to have had "an inordinate fondness for beetles"? One might think it was Charles Darwin: the huge variety of beetles was, after all, an early passion of his. But the credit for what Stephen Jay Gould called "the most widely quoted one-liner in evolutionary biology" actually goes to JBS Haldane (1892-1964) the revered British geneticist, Marxist and wit. A theologian had asked him what could be inferred about the mind of God from the works of His creation. Haldane was pleased with his answer and employed it several times in his writing.

As he spoke, the beetles numbered more than 400,000 known species (compared with some 8,000 mammals) and no doubt a few more thousand have been discovered since. Along with some 9,000 birds there are the millions of bacteria and viruses to which have now been added the archaea, microscopic life forms often inhabiting the planet's most extreme environments.

Knowledge of the natural world's variety grows greater every day, along with human threats to it. In his recent inaugural homily, Pope Francis said: "Let us be protectors of creation, protectors of God's plan inscribed in nature, protectors of one another and of the environment." Even his choice of name evokes not only special empathy with the poor but feeling for the animal kingdom. St Francis, as a Franciscan website describes, "would find himself in an ecstasy of prayer with eyes raised to heaven while holding a waterfowl in his hands".

Yes, but what should be expected of the new pope and his church in today's fraught interplay of religion and science? In an editorial last month, the international journal Nature looked forward to hearing from Pope Francis on scientific issues. "Contrary to widespread belief," it asserted, "the modern Catholic Church is science-friendly…The church's strong support for Darwinian evolution, for example, contrasts sharply with the backwards, unscientific belief in creationism of many US evangelicals and lawmakers – a concept Pope Benedict XVI rightly criticised in 2007 as 'absurd'."

That evangelical creationism is also alive and well on this island was confirmed in recent news about the opening of the new visitor centre at the Giant's Causeway in Co Antrim. Alongside the centre's mainstream geological history of the basalt's volcanic origins, one audio guide explains that "some people around the world and specifically in Northern Ireland" prefer to seek its origins in the Book of Genesis. The British Centre for Science Education, a counter creationist group, has called the North the "European capital of creationism".

The editorial in Nature, however, was perhaps overeager in welcoming Pope Benedict's view of evolution. What he actually found an "absurdity" was to argue that accepting the scientific proofs in favour of evolution and believing in a role for God were necessarily mutually exclusive. Evolution, Benedict went on, "does not answer the great philosophical question, 'Where does everything come from?'"

Ireland has its own priestly enthusiast for science in Fr Seán McDonagh, the Columban missionary who has spent thirty years promoting ecological awareness and in criticism of his church's delayed and weakly framed support for it. Last month, on the eve of change in the papacy, he wrote in the US National Catholic Reporter about the Vatican's failure to address climate change with urgency and, despite an "increased sprinkling of ecological language and concerns", to make proper use of scientific data. Papal teaching on ecology, McDonagh chided, has been "almost exclusively homocentric", focused on human benefit and supremacy. "It is important theologically to remember that God has a history with nature that is independent of God's relationship with humanity," he said.

This connects with ideas strongly current since the deep-ecology movement gained momentum, especially in the US, in the late twentieth century. The term was coined in 1973 by Arne Naess, a Norwegian philosopher who argued that the value of non-human life and its ecosystems is independent of its usefulness to human beings – the rainforests and their species have a prior right to exist regardless of whether they hold medicines for human welfare. A seeking for affinity with the rest of nature was his ideal of human fulfilment.

Since then, the benefits of "ecosystem services" to humans has come to dominate the reason for conserving other species. On the other hand, Prof James Lovelock's theory of Gaia – Earth as an intricately self-sustaining system – has encouraged deep ecologists to see that the planet could do very well without us. Their aspirations have meshed better with other, mainly eastern spiritualities than with those of Rome.

Amiable atheists like me, meanwhile, randomly adrift on an accidental planet, are left to relish our place in a multitude of life forms, all coined by chance and polished or casually extinguished by natural selection.

The whole thing is a transient but enchanting mystery. And one can always lift one's eyes from the beetles to the stars – for which, as Haldane added, God seems to have shown an equal affection.

April 13ᵗʰ 2013

Breach of the seasons

As the month began, the wind went north for a while, as if to confess more honestly its Arctic origins.

Then it switched back east to the white-slashed mountains and wherever it is that planes start from to stretch their frosty plumes across the sky.

The wind scoured a hillside spread with ewes-in-waiting, each lying down in her own maternal patch. They were tupped last November, to match lambing to the first spring grass, but found themselves couched instead on pastures grazed to the nap and bleached to shades of khaki.

After weeks without rain, their droppings dotted the bare ground in dry and constipated dollops, but the ewes themselves had never looked finer, fleeces clean, fluffy and blow-dried – perforce – to perfection.

Their first few lambs, detergent-white, stayed close in the lee of their mothers or were taken tenderly into barns at night to be warmed in an infrared glow.

My farming neighbours, hollow-eyed from restless torchlight patrols, were at least spared the tears of their brothers in snow-pillowed Ulster and Wales. The west, they agreed, has had the best of it, a brassy sun mocking us often from dawn to dusk.

Things have changed by now, as the pent-up reservoir of rain begins to sweep back from the ocean. A brief simulacrum of spring may precede a brief gesture at summer – who knows any more? The pace of natural change itself has changed, on a planet not used to being hurried.

Reared on eternities of whirling gases, the slow spread of deserts and infinite millennia of ice, it reacts to having its atmosphere upset in mere centuries, even decades. As we melt the sea ice from the poles, the Arctic jet streams swing south in a tizzy of circumpolar aberration.

The birds are finding their voice at sunrise again, though the chorus sounds quite a bit thinner. A month or more ago, they couldn't wait to get started on the spring: thrushes up poles, blackbirds on bushes, wrens ghetto-blasting Bach from the hedge. There was a silence for a long while, as if the hillside had been struck dumb with cold, but now the right sounds have been creeping back, among them the shrill delirium of lambs at play.

One I have been missing is the drone of bumblebees.

There are my broad beans, safely overwintered in the tunnel and now in tall, scented bloom, but few enough bees find their way in for a pollinating fumble at the flowers.

The trees on the acre, meanwhile, have done their best to ignore this year's breach of the seasons. Each species is long conditioned by its biogeography, so that trees from the south of Europe tend to stick to old habits of budburst in the spring.

As April began, for example, still well in the grip of frost, the sycamore buds were already cracking to show a peep of catkin, and the horse chestnut was already sporting full quadruple coronets of leaves.

The alder, meanwhile, was prizing its first two leaves apart here and there; native oak and ash, frosty memories embedded in their genes, kept their buds tight and dark. "Oak before ash, a bit of a splash; ash before oak, we're in for a soak" – the ash is nearly always last, but the soak comes anyway.

For years I have recorded this progress into leaf, for digital analysis elsewhere. Phenology, the study of cyclic happenings in nature, was once the passion of country naturalists with notebooks, but it is now a sterner science, bonded to ecology and the futurology of climate change.

First leaves, flowers, frogspawn, bumblebees and migrant birds were once measures of spring's arrival – indeed, such events were a guarantee of God's seasons, fit for Christian clergy to record. Now they chart the story of a world in which nature's co-ordinates are failing.

Evolutionary timetables narrowed over thousands of years are jolted out of sync, disrupted differentially by global warming. Birds are missing their seasonal appointments with caterpillars, fish with their crucial hatch of plankton.

This icy March for Europe may seem to contradict the trend of warmer, earlier springs, but it was a regional, atmospheric phenomenon (like so many extreme weather events) triggered by the warming at the poles.

So Ireland's contribution to European phenology goes on, focused in particular on the advancing date of spring, more dramatic and measurable than changes in the autumn dates of fruiting, leaf fall, hibernation and so on.

The Irish Phenology Network, based at Trinity College Dublin, has a nationwide spread of gardens monitoring the habits of the same tree species now being watched across Europe, and other gardens keeping tabs on a range of native Irish species: ten plants, five birds and five insects.

Anyone can offer more records through Nature Watch. (You'll find its website at biodiversityireland.ie.) "Spring is here!" announced its website on 28 February. "At least in the south of Ireland…"

They might like to start that again.

April 20th 2013
Why the thrush trills

Back on duty as soon as the rising temperature allowed, a song thrush has been waiting on the same branch, morning after morning, to share with me his audition for the spring. Quite which of the 100-odd phrases in its repertoire I've walked in on I can't judge without a sonogram, but there he is, perched above my head and holding me immobile and marvelling. Watching that slim beak parting and closing in such precise and deliberate clarity, I am spellbound once again by the beauty and mystery of birdsong.

Knowing what it's for – the territorial proclamation – just compounds the puzzle. If the thrush settled merely for "F***off, f***off, f***off!" (as, no doubt, some bird, somewhere in the world, can be heard, more or less, to do) what would happen to my wonder? Why these elaborately tuneful arpeggios, just to differentiate its mating claim on a clump of rural roadside?

As we head, at long last, into some simulation of spring, I turn the question around. Why should I, as passing human, give a damn what the bird is doing, let alone aspire to share the "first fine, careless rapture" that Browning once awarded it?

Never have so many Irish people been so aware of the rest of nature, its infinite detail and diversity, or of the urgent imperative of conservation. But has the appeal to our feelings been far too shy? Nature's offering of "eco-system services" is the widely urged rationale for conservation. But this so often puts the material and economic benefits first, while deeper and nobler human needs and loves are almost a concessionary afterthought.

May11ᵗʰ 2013

Insect spotting

One of the good days brought a swallow and a hoverfly into the same frame of my delight, the first zooming past the gable just to let me know they were back, the second frozen in the air like a jewelled Higgs boson before changing co-ordinates in the usual quantum instant.

Goodness knows what the swallows have been eating, arriving to such chilled and empty Irish air, but hoverflies, with their gifts of bilocation, up, down or sideways, have never made it easy for birds.

We need all the insects this spring and all the springs – our 180 different hoverflies, 101 native bumble and solitary bees, our countless moths and wasps. Never mind the ban on neonicotinoid sprays – though the EU has had the right idea – we need to watch out for all our pollinating insects, not just the honeybees that do the media-appearances side of the job.

To excite public interest in the whereabouts and well-being of our nectar-loving insects, the Irish Pollinator Initiative website of the National Biodiversity Data Centre offers ten insects to look out for as the weather warms up – an encouragement to get your eye in, as it were.

At the top of the list is a colourful rarity, the tawny mining bee (Andrena fulva), rediscovered in Kilkenny and Wicklow last summer after more than eighty years of seeming extinction. Look for the female, clothed in bright red hairs, as she burrows into the lawn, raising a little volcano of excavated spoil.

The hairy-footed flower bee – isn't that lovely? – or Anthrophora plumipes hasn't been confirmed in Ireland yet, but is probably heading this way from the warmer gardens of England. A lover of flowers in the mint family, it can nest by the hundred in south-facing cliffs.

Among other imminent immigrants, given climate change, is the tree bumblebee (Bombus hypnorum), already building up its numbers on the Welsh coast, sometimes in the comfort of garden nesting boxes.

Hanging on in Ireland, just about, is the great yellow bumblebee (Bombus distinguendus) that once thrived in the hay meadows of the west, its long tongue tailored to the deep florets of red clover and knapweed. Since hay gave way to early-mown silage, and flowery meadows were resown with ryegrass, this bee is on the verge of extinction, thriving only in a few pockets of north Mayo's Mullet peninsula.

Records of the small heath bumblebee (Bombus jonellus), once common on our coastal dunes and moorlands, seem also to have fallen off drastically, and learning the sequence of its football-jersey stripes is good practice for sorting the more common bumblebees of our gardens.

Another speciality of dunes on our east and southeast coasts is the ginger-haired solitary bee Osmia aurulenta – "fantastic to watch in action" promises the Pollinator Initiative website, presumably as it exits from its nests in empty snail shells.

The four hoverflies, or Syrphidae, "to look for" are plucked from the formidable database of Dr Martin Speight, long the leading entomologist with the National Parks and Wildlife Service. (He notably named his website Syrph the Net.) First hoverfly choice for beginners (and remains among them, for all my pleasure in the insects' brilliance and variety) is one prettily banded with gold. Episyrphus balteatus is also anthropophilic, meaning that it's happy almost anywhere, even around people, and helps by eating aphids on growing cereals as well as by visiting, and thus pollinating, a wide range of white and yellow flowers.

E balteatus not only lives in Ireland, and is seen on the wing as early as February, but is often overtaken in numbers by vast swarms of migrants from southern Europe.

The migration of flies in any self-directed way is an idea that takes some getting used to. Indeed, the swarms of E balteatus arriving – on the same wind as red admiral butterflies – from the sea at Courtmacsherry Bay, in Co Cork, in July 1995 were the first such event on Irish record. But this and a few other European species are regular migrants – E balteatus has even arrived alive (if rather pointlessly) on Arctic ice floes.

It also figures in one of my favourite accounts of migration, that of the British ornithologist David Lack in his Enjoying Ornithology (1965). Almost disbelievingly, he and his wife watched flocks of finches, linnets and other small birds flying southwards through one of the highest and narrowest passes of the Pyrenees, often only inches above the ground. With them were unending processions of clouded yellow butterflies, red admirals and dragonflies. But outnumbering them all were swarms of gold-and-black hoverflies, later identified as Episyrphus balteatus. "The whole surface of the pass," he wrote, "was a shimmer of iridescent light, due to the reflections of the autumn sun on myriad tiny wings."

June 1ˢᵗ 2013
A relationship with a stream

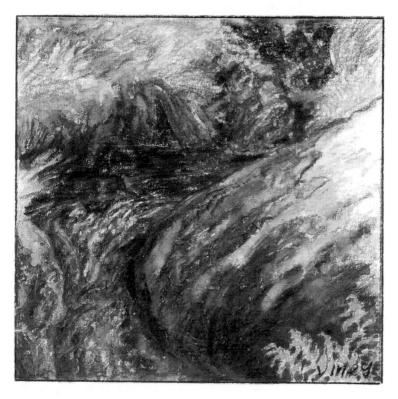

The rig arrived straight after breakfast to squat hugely inside the gate. I cowered in the kitchen and then fled to my desk, overawed by the machine's risen tower and the ensuing remorseless rumble and chatter of the drill.

As it chewed through yellow clay, into gravel and boulders, and down into Ordovician sandstone, sandbags were ringed to usher its rocky eruption away through the trees.

Well before lunchtime (we had feared it might be days), after a last gasp and whistle of compressed air, the gush of water was declared good and sufficient – even bountiful – at sixty-seven metres below the garden path.

Thus, regretfully, with our energies now dwindling for sorties up the hill, we have swapped our long bond with the stream for the mutter of an underground pump.

From the swirl, bubble and rush of water freshly distilled from sea and sky we have switched like our neighbours to the buried pulse of percolating groundwater, squeezing darkly downhill through fissures and cracks. An artesian well does not, after all, tap into some underground secret crystal pool but is topped up continually from descending squirts and trickles in the rock.

The stream, on the other hand, gathers its beginnings from a basin of bog below the ridge. There it carves deep runnels in the peat, rehearsing an erosion that, farther down the hillside, has carved wide ravines, over hundreds of years, in the assorted debris of glacial till.

One of these grassy valleys, tilting up across the road, offered us early lessons in self-sufficiency in our waterless, cisternless, Land Commission cottage.

The stream, it's true, ducking under the bridge, emerged in a hollow it had carved across a corner of our acre: we could always climb up and down with a bucket. But, following our neighbours at that time, we turned to gravity: a one-inch pipe unfurled far up the hill and plunged into the right sort of pool at the right sort of angle, the end well wrapped in a filtering gauze and held down with a rock.

There are little pools above huge boulders that terrace the stream into mossy waterfalls and much bigger pools, scooped out by floods, below them.

Sometimes little pools can be made bigger by making a dam with a borrowed rock or two, and sods of turf torn from the bank.

The weather was always sunny, with a breeze off the islands in a bright blue sea.

Lambs nuzzled their mothers, and wheatears bobbed on every rock. The stream babbled and sparkled around me. And once – I have this on record – Ethna came up the hill with hot buttered scones in a napkin, and a Thermos of hot coffee.

The days of this schoolboy construction were among the happiest of my life. But then, of course, would come the flash floods my coffee waitress had reminded me of, rolling rocks like cannonballs smashing the dam away. A day or two afterwards the water would fall back, exposing both my folly and the dry end of the pipe.

A long drought, too, could reduce the stream to a trickle and prompt a sudden sigh from the kitchen tap. The trips up the hill required balletic leaps between the crests of grassed-over ancient lazy beds – a movement to startle the grazing ewes. A few would squat in fright, their pee scorching further brown patches in the turf.

It took many years, indeed, to find a way to wriggle the pipe around the boulder to a lodgment that never ran dry. I endured frustrations with the airlock, that fatal bubble, or column thereof, swallowed and sucked down to lodge at some stubborn undulation.

"Is it there yet? … Well, it bloody should be!" This, before the mobile phone, could need several trips down and up again.

At times Ethna, in pity, or a forgivable fit of corrective zeal, would take over the feeding of water into the top of the pipe at just the right angle to coax more streams of bubbles up. It took patience, especially while crouching, ano-raked, in the rain or, in Paul Durcan's treasured image, "backside to the wind".

We shall, nonetheless, miss our close, even primal relationship with the stream, so alive and chaotic yet willing to be tamed.

Even filtered and UV sterilised en route (as it later seemed wise to do), a glass of diamond-bright water, fresh from the sky and ready chilled, has been part of the privilege of "another life".

The well adds to a national total of rather more than 100,000 and will end the emergency of such floods and droughts as the climate has up its sleeve. What its water will taste like we wait to know, when the man has come, as promised, to put in the pump.

July 13th 2013
An orgy of snails

The dense, drizzly coastal fog that is often our share of summer high pressure enveloped the Thallabawn hillside for three days, leaving every leaf glistening with water, every flower stem bowed with the weight of it. Such perfect conditions for slug and snail activity brought obvious thoughts to a gardener, but the naturalist in me had other concerns. As, for example, whether Cepaea nemoralis might still be "at it" down in the dunes, today mere shadows in the Labradorian gloom.

The mass mating of the sandy snails is more a phenomenon of soft days in late spring. Their celebratory orgy can then be so abundant that it's hard to know where to tread without trampling some entwined and frothy ecstasy. Much of it belongs to Helix aspersa, the so-called garden snail that here builds its shell from the powdered calcium of its cast-up ocean cousins – a truly economic recycling.

But while its shell in our gardens is a glossy nut brown, in the dunes it is often quite matt and blueish, this from its sand-blasted winter hibernation in the crevices of rocks and driftwood fences.

Cepaea nemoralis, on the other hand, its co-celebrant in these fertility rites, has spent the winter nestled in the moss or sand, so that only the top whorl or two of its shell has been bleached and worn to white by the constant sift of wind-blown grains. But the colour and pattern of the spiral-banded shell is notoriously variable.

As the fog dissipated, on the fourth day, I went on a foray across the channel and into the dunes, scattering the rabbits and nesting larks. There, indeed, were couples of Cepaea still in the tight lock of mating. A little delicate disturbance showed the undersides of the shells were yellow, when they might equally well have been pink or brown.

The sheer prettiness of these banded snails is enough to earn one's interest, But the distribution and variability of Cepaea has obsessed scientists for close on a century. Only last month, two biologists at Nottingham University, Dr Angus Davison and a PhD student, Adele Grindon, offered strong probability that the snails were brought to Ireland with Mesolithic travellers from the eastern Pyrenees, who used them as takeaway food.

There is a continuous fossil record of the snails in Ireland for at least 8,000 years, and this new study of the genetic history ("mitochondrial phylogenies") of living Cepaea populations across the whole of Europe showed most of those of the Irish west coast to be quite different from those, say, in Britain.

Their European match was found only in a restricted region of the eastern Pyrenees, with a few scattered examples from near Toulouse, in southwest France, and the Isle of Man, and a single specimen from Wales.

The resulting research is confidently titled: "Irish Cepaea nemoralis land snails have a cryptic Franco-Iberian origin that is most easily explained by the movements of Mesolithic humans".

It offers yet more evidence from DNA detective work that many early arrivals of migrant life in Ireland, whether human, plant, molluscan or mammal, came from Iberia rather than across the Irish Sea.

Back in the 1950s, Cepaea's local permutations of shell banding and colour prompted a quite acrimonious debate among biologists studying evolution. Were the differences the result of random "genetic drift" over the centuries, or of natural selection? One powerful argument, backed up by experiment, for the influence of selection was that the snails' main predator – song thrushes – were less likely to seize upon snails whose shell colour most matched their background vegetation.

But Cepaea has been good for yet another twist – this quite literally, in sometimes spiralling anti-clockwise instead of the right-hand turn more usual in helical snails. In the 1920s, two British conchologists, Prof Arthur Boycott and Capt Cyril Diver, made an expedition to Bundoran, Co Donegal, to hunt for sinistral (left-handed) Cepaea. They had noted that many such specimens in British and Irish museum collections had come from the Finner dunes, where "old peasant women" collected empty shells by the thousand to make twopenny necklaces for the tourists.

The two men stalked the dunes, where the wind had sieved out shells from the sandhills and heaped them together in the slacks. In one small area "the size of a tennis-lawn" there were about 200,000. They spent a morning going through 8,000 of them, and the 6,021st was sinistral – the only one. Then they found a live left-handed Cepaea on the roadside outside Ballyshannon – but whether they crossed it with a dextral partner, and what the result was I cannot say. When last heard of, they were seeking collaborators in a further systematic scrutiny of shells, "aiming at numbers of the order of 100,000 or even half a million".

August 3rd 2013
Swirling swarms and virgin queens

In all that heat last month, and near enough to the silly season, these islands conjured not a single insect "plague". No kamikaze squadrons of water beetles hammered the bonnets of shiny cars, mistaking them for ponds.

No clouds of migrant ladybirds sent bathers shrieking from the beaches. No hordes of wasps pursued lickers of ice creams as they fled from St Stephen's Green. (Indeed, where are the wasps? I haven't seen one for weeks.) For a really significant Irish insect plague, one could go back to 1688, when millions of cockchafers – "maybugs" – arrived on the coast of Connemara, borne, most improbably, on a southwest wind. Their locust-like progress inland, as far as Headford, was recorded by Dr Thomas Molyneux, one of the most active and observant Irish naturalists of his day.

"A short while after their coming," he wrote, "they had so entirely eat up and destroy'd all the leaves of the trees for some miles round about, that the whole country, tho' it was in the middle of summer, was left as bare and naked as if it had been in the depths of winter [and] the grinding of the leaves in the mouths of this multitude all together, made a sound very much resembling the sawing of timber…" In due course, their "spawn" became fat white grubs underground, devouring the roots of corn, so that "the poorer sort of the native Irish (the country then labouring under a scarcity of provision) had a way of dressing them and lived upon them as food." This could interest the current advocates of mass insect consumption, if already echoed in the historical diet of Australian Aborigines.

The spectacular migration of cockchafers, as Molyneux guessed, originated in France and stemmed from their own search for food. An abundance of food, on the other hand, can produce a population explosion. In 2009, millions of painted lady butterflies arrived in Britain and Ireland – "snowing" butterflies in parts of this island. The original source was the Atlas Mountains of Morocco, where the wettest winter in decades had produced a forest of thistles, the food plant of the butterfly. The extra thousands of pupae launched the first northward pulse of this continuously breeding species.

In Ireland, a totally natural and regular mechanism produces an annual swarming of ants in the sky, a phenomenon celebrated over Dublin in high, ecstatic swirlings of the city's swifts, starling and gulls, feasting as they fly.

It occurs over several afternoons about now; may, indeed, already have happened, if humidity, wind speed and temperature were right. It is triggered by an astonishing synchrony of body clocks in millions of ants in thousands of separate colonies.

A colony grows from the eggs laid by a mated queen. These hatch initially into workers, whose job is to forage and feed more larvae. As the colony matures in size, it prepares to reproduce itself by producing winged ants, both males and virgin queens.

The synchronised swarming of the nuptial flights brings together young virgin queens and males from miles away, thus refreshing the species' genes. The swarms are also big enough to tilt the odds against any individual queen being eaten by a bird. The males are dead within hours, but the queens, often mating several times with different partners, spin back to earth and cut off their wings.

They are ready to start a new colony.

In Dublin's city parks and under sun-warmed garden paths of the suburbs, the black ant is generally the common one, while in the countryside it is mostly the yellow meadow ant that rises from the fields. Back in the 1930s, the naturalist Robert Lloyd Praeger encountered their swarms as he walked into Blessington, Co Wicklow.

"They became more abundant on nearing the village," he wrote (in A Populous Solitude, published in 1941), "and I roughly estimated that on the last half-mile of road over a million-and-a-half of ants were crawling, while in the air above the road they were so abundant that my clothes were quite brown with them.

"The fields on each side were thick with them, the windows of the hotel were alive with them, and my tea was richly flavoured with them. Unless they were confined to a narrow line down which I had the fortune to walk, there must have been hundreds of millions of them within a mile of Blessington."

Around the village today, such a density of colonies is found only in the last few vestiges of old and permanent grassland. Here, left undisturbed, yellow ants carry particles of soil to build their small, free-draining mounds, angled to the warmth of the sun.

Most Irish farmland is now a quilt of intensive silage fields, ploughed and reseeded with ryegrass and compacted by machinery – no landscape for the industry of Lasius flavus or its annual flights of sacrificial bliss.

August 17th 2013

Playing the wandering fool

The long calms and offshore breezes of this summer have let the sea put back even more of its offshore store of sand than it sucked away last winter – an exceptional annual bonus in its rolling budget of sediment.

This new hem of the strand is fluffy and smooth and so soft that my boots sink into it. The splay-footed, duck-shaped trail they leave still embarrasses me. Other men leave proper, manly, parallel prints: why do my feet go like that? "Why can't you walk straight and not keep swerving into me?" (this from my older brother, long ago, but I remember where it was, in the lane beside the gasworks).

Never mind. Sometimes, in winter, with no one around to bump into, I have walked the strand for ages with my eyes shut, relying on hearing to guide me. My advance is always into the sun, poised low above Connemara across the bay, so that the vermilion light in my eyelids offers one compass and the whisper of surf beside me another. My course does swerve, indeed, but I have never actually walked into the sea. Everyone, at some time, should have the space and freedom to play the wandering fool.

Finding interesting stuff means walking the strand every day, summer and winter, as I used to when younger and everything was new. It was then I accumulated most of the biological bric-a-brac that lines our window sills – skulls, shells, fossils and the rest – and the gaudy plastic trawler balls now strung into pillars of colour at the woodshed. Either the trawlers have stopped losing them, or using them, or my beachcombing mornings are now too few; but I have more than enough to brighten a winter garden.

The length of Ireland's coastline must now, I suppose, be nearing some kind of exactitude, as Earth is scanned obsessively by robots in the sky. But everything depends on where you pace it, and at what moment. Tide lifts and falls; foam reaches up to lick one's boots or curl around a rock. For the beach lovers the boundary of land and ocean is more a state of mind than any line drawn in the sand.

October 12ᵗʰ 2013

A moth on my pyjamas

Moths of a warm autumn nuzzle my lighted window, their little eyes glittering like rubies. Sometimes I leave it open, to see what might wander in. I think of my childhood terror of some furry-headed intruder bouncing around the walls of my bedroom, and how sad there was no one in the family to effect, as it were, some intelligent attempt at introduction, rather than swiping wildly with a rolled-up magazine.

The moth that came in the other night settled quietly on my pyjama sleeve – the arm propping up a Henning Mankel – and seemed content just to gaze into the chilly brilliance of my LED reading lamp.

There is much to be learned about the different wavelengths of light, whether from candle flame or light-emitting diode, and their differential reception by the multipronged antennae of different moths, but I think I can give it a miss. My moth may have seen the bulb as a moon or star, by which to navigate, or as the sun, by which to go to sleep – and that, by the comfortable stillness of its perch, seemed likely.

What held my own gaze, at the short squint to my bicep, was the utterly beautiful iridescence of its closed underwings – a cool, antique sort of glow, like old church brass. That, and its smallness for a moth, its vertically closed wings perhaps a centimetre high. Keen to see their upper sides, which is what the books provide, I nudged its tail. The glimpse this offered, in the moth's panicky retreat into the (inedible) curtains, was of a dark brown geometry like a 1930s armchair. There are far too many rows of closely similar wings on the pages of moth-identification guides, so I went back to the latest sinister plot twist in Sweden.

The beauty, diversity and frequent mystery of moths are beginning to find a popular response, prompted by new websites that offer photographs of live moths in the field. Mothsireland.com is the one for recording sightings and distribution maps; irishmoths.net offers a gorgeous gallery from Jenny Seawright, photographed mostly in her garden in Co Cork. At the other end of the island, Robert Thompson's photographs in the Ulster Museum's Butterflies and Moths of Northern Ireland are among the most dazzling ever made.

All this is far from the pioneering years of Irish entomology in the early

1800s, when collectors haunted the woods of Killarney to practise "sugaring" as the new way of trapping moths. They perfected their own treacle mixes (such as molasses with brown ale or rum), brushed on to tree trunks at dusk before the moths began to fly. Even better was an empty beehive smeared on the outside with honey. Today's recipes add a mash of over-ripe bananas.

Higher-tech enthusiasts use the mercury-vapour light trap. This draws moths to its intense illumination, then sifts them through a funnel to settle in empty egg boxes, for leisurely morning inspection. Afterwards, you tuck them safely into a bush, sometimes wishing there weren't quite so many all at once.

In the summer of last year, an Anglo-Irish team of lepidopterists worked up to ten light traps a night and tramped dunes, marsh and farmland to search out caterpillars, all to survey the moths of Belmullet Peninsula, in Co Mayo. One June night their traps lured seventy-six species of macro moth (that is, the larger species), such as Map-winged Swift, Oblique Carpet, Brussels Lace, Dark Brocade and Pinion-streaked Snout – names demanding their capitals and drawn from the long and earnest history of sugarers and honey smearers.

The macro moths of Ireland include the lovely day-flying Emperor of heathered hills and the pink-flushed elephant hawkmoth, whose big, fuchsia-nibbling caterpillar is pictured each August in puzzled "strange creature" emails to Eye on Nature. It overwinters in a chestnut-brown pupa, and there is online advice for keeping one in a jam jar for hatching next spring.

My little brassy moth was clearly one of a legion of micro moths, whose wingspan, in an arbitrary ordering, is no more than twenty millimetres. To grasp the delicacy of collecting, displaying and identifying such insects, find the YouTube video of a young woman using tweezers and hair-fine pins to stretch one out on its polystyrene mortuary slab.

Micro moths do have some fascinating aeronautical forms. A few are like ghostly wisps of thistledown, some have bushy tails, others spread wings like Japanese fans, still more could be early designs for flying machines. One can see – just about, at that size – the charms of obsession with micro moth collection.

The Natural History Museum in London has 1.5 million specimens, pinned and spread by collectors since the mid-eighteenth century.

They must have had ways, I presume, of stopping the moths getting at them.

November 16ᵗʰ 2013

Oil paints and driftwood sculptures

One day soon I must paint something big and red. Otherwise what were they for, these pricey tubes of alizarin and cadmium red deep? A little alizarin goes a long way, like purple blood. I could leak some into a bog painting just now, for the smouldering hues of November. Or do some crimson fields for drama – I've always had trouble with greens.

These overexuberant tubes of red are as good as when I bought them, almost forty years ago, stocking up in Kennedy's of Harcourt Street in Dublin for the big move west.

So are most of the wood-carving chisels for the driftwood sculptures I thought I might do, and the grits for polishing beach pebbles in a barrel spun by the stream (no end to creativity once my time was all my own).

A modest graphic talent had been nagging since childhood, along with the rush of pleasure in colour and form. In my newspaper years I spent lunchtimes in the Dublin galleries, being happily tutored by my art critic colleague and friend Brian Fallon.

I hung around real painters, let them tell me to stick with what I was good at. Real painters don't spend their lives spinning words; they put paint first.

The big deal about moving west was not, of course, just the urge to self-taught self-expression but a hazard at surviving somewhere beautiful. (Much the same thing, it might be said.) But discovering that days were finite, after all, was the first big reckoning of the "alternative" lifestyle.

The priority was feeding a family, taming an acre and mastering spillet and sleán. Only many years later, sans goats, hens and bees, did I finally get down to painting.

This was not without further procrastination, probably born of fear. Our riveting landscape was prodigiously unpaintable – you'd need a canvas like a Cinemascope screen. What could you do with these great sweeps of sand, sea and sky, with not a decent vertical in sight? Looking the other way, to the hills, there were all these miserable greens, either offensively dead on the canvas or far too shrill with nitrogen fertiliser.

Besides, I had still had "nowhere" to paint (now at one end of a little room shared with seed box, chainsaw, computer and whatever else needs a home).

But then, once, I accompanied a real painter, Derek Hill, to an island where, perched on a stool, he captured a landscape of barest essentials – a glimmering line of sand between sea and sky, a single cloud rising from a dull hill – conjuring immensities of light and distance on the back of a cigar box lid eight inches by six.

The impressionists pioneered painting outdoors and didn't seem to mind the light changing every five minutes. I don't know what David Hockney does about midges. (Perhaps that's why he's gone so digital.)

And I admire Scotland's great Joan Eardley, lugging huge canvases to paint the waves, her easel lashed against the wind.

After a few dogged expeditions, my box easel loaded with paints and hefted from one hand to another, I settled for sketches, photographs and memories of light – or whatever was framed by a window.

Even set free to work on a Monday or Thursday I remain essentially a captive "Sunday" painter, shackled to scenery and painting stuff more or less as it looks.

I have fits of disillusion at failing to find any personal vision: something arousingly beyond what's simply there. In the age of the iPad camera where's the point in rehashing Paul Henry or Corot, not to mention half Cambridge's window, when the power and dark magic of the west lie in the mind and eye of a Seán McSweeney or Brian Bourke? They are real painters; always were. Without nature they would be lost – but nature reborn as art.

There have never been more real painters in this country thanks to the cultural aspirations of Charles Haughey. He was Medici or Malraux, perhaps a bit of both, and his tax reliefs and open regard for art helped nourish a transfusion of aesthetic sensibility. This put paintings into gallery windows in every small town and tourist village.

And if a lot of them spring from self-taught Sunday industry, their bright enjoyment and effort enrich the national psyche.

All kinds of prominent people surprise us with a private passion for painting. Here in Mayo it has been almost a political freemasonry, engaging, among others, President Hillery, the late John Healy and the current Pádraig Flynn.

November 30ᵗʰ 2013

Warming globe, shifting sands

At the bend in the road at the top of the hill the summer tourists tread hard on the brakes, not so much for caution as in sudden awe of the view. It is partly the grand spread of it all – so much landscape at once – but partly its near-primitive disposition.

There's the size of the strand, for a start, sprawling back around the dunes to a big lawn of level, grassy machair; then the channel of the mountain river, winding through the sand. This curls back to a couple of lakes or lagoons, one glittering under a low, wooded cliff with a plateau of bog beyond. All this is virtually roadless and couched below the mountains as if for revelation: Mweelrea on this side, lofty Benwhatsit across in Connemara.

The mouth of the fjord, Killary Harbour, opens darkly in between.

The soft bits of Thallabawn are distinctly dynamic, their sculpting and shifting over the centuries ruled by wind and wave. A map from 1838 shows dunes at either end of the strand but great tongues of bare sand licking far back into the shore. By 1919 the dunes had grown across from the south, and the machair and lakes were forming behind them. But the little graveyard perched on the northern dunes was now an isolated pyramid in the sand.

This "burial mound", as everyone knew it, has since been melted by storms into a flat mandala of stone slabs. The dunes have been trimmed back and cliffed on the seaward side. A new rampart of rocks has been built to resist the flood when spring tide and swollen river combine to attack the lowest, sandy pastures. A farmer tried to persuade the channel to take a more direct course to the sea – he took his digger to the strand and carved a new course for it, straight out. The tides erased it, and the channel resumed its leisurely loop of an estuary: it is where it wants to go.

So, even without global warming, this soft stretch of the west has known enormous change, as storms, tides and currents have played with available sediments – offshore sand and gravel swept out in the melt of the glaciers or carried down in the river from the mountain. A summer as calm as the last one let the waves build up the strand – a new soft and fluffy selvedge at the edge.

The autumn gales have been clawing the sand back again, the breakers spinning like wheels. Looking out from my desk I wonder, of course, how far fiercer and steeper storm-piled waves will bring a rising sea.

Round and over the dunes, I suppose, into the lakes, and as far as the reedy marsh where the hillside rock begins to rise. I shan't see it, but somebody will.

With Ireland taking much of the brunt of Europe's future Atlantic storms, our coastline has been under close study since the late 1970s. Ireland's leading authority on likely sea-level impact is Dr Robert Devoy, professor of geography at University College Cork's Coastal and Marine Research Centre. For the immediate future, his work is relatively reassuring. Much of our coast, as he describes, already has high resilience, conditioned to environmental extremes of big tides, frequent storms and heavy rainfall.

Our western continental shelf, the inshore shallows that run into rocky platforms, and our wide and often island-studded bays all help to blunt and dissipate the power of hurricane-heaped Atlantic swells and slow initial erosion from a rising sea level.

Even so, about a third of coastal wetlands like the one below me seem doomed to disappear. Erosion already bites hardest at the soft cliffs of glacial till at the southeast corner of the island, averaging as much as a metre a year. But the south and east coasts at least have an abundant supply of sediment for the beaches, lying in banks offshore.

Elsewhere, the supply from these old glacial deposits has almost ceased. Instead, sand and gravel in beach barriers are being swept along the shore and dissipated, and tractorloads scooped up for construction have robbed the budget further.

How fast will the sea level rise? A survey of ninety sea-level experts in eighteen countries, just published, offers a consensus of between forty and sixty centimetres in this century if the human world takes determined action to limit carbon dioxide, and between seventy and 120 centimetres if it does not. Devoy, like all his colleagues, wrestles with the uncertainties of modelling, melting ice and political commitment. He does, however, think it's time – long, long past time – we prepared for it.

Integrated coastal zone management, well discussed through the 1990s and strongly urged by Europe, would bang heads together in the several Government departments concerned, and involve coastal communities as stakeholders. University College Cork's website on the subject, however, has found nothing new to say since 2004.

I think, while there's time, I must walk to the far lake and listen to the whooper swans gossiping under the cliff.

January 18th 2014

After the storms

The wilder the shore, the more natural the impact of stormy seas. It's only when man-made works are undermined or demolished – sea walls, car parks, cemeteries, Mesolithic middens – that there's much headline stuff to report. Thus, news of natural change at Thallabawn is offered tardily, with deference to more troubling human costs elsewhere. Besides, getting into my waders to ford the river channel is becoming a bit of a struggle.

First signs of inundation: far-flung tidelines of seaweed and plastic bottles in the fields behind the strand and a long way up the boreen between them. First signs of wind speed: tawny curtains of dead marram grass, wrenched from the dunes, cladding every fence along the shore. Plus sheets of plastic borne from Connemara, across the bay. Then lifebuoy posts at drunken angles, newly bereft of their lifebuoys.

Coastal erosion, of course, around at the seaward side: great shark bites into the dunes, spilling random gobbets of sand and marram. Scattered around them, sea pink cushions snatched from the tops of far island cliffs. A few bare driftwood tree trunks, rushed ashore too soon to grow any glimmer of gooseneck barnacles. Leisurely tides may bring stranger things. (Achill had a big fin whale.)

Just one drowned sheep, or what the ravens had bloodily left of it, lay in a tattered mattress of wool. But below the ravaged scarp of the dunes, on scallops of new sand, the hieroglyphs of wildlife tracks brought the same news as always: the dainty commas of pattering rabbits, pursued, here and there, by an early morning fox; the careful, Greek-graceful prints of an otter. The take-off tracks of a burdened black-backed gull hinted at a hungry swoop to the sand, but out at the edge of an ebbing tide, the little flocks of sanderlings sifted to and fro, undisturbed. After storms, life, and death, go on as normal.

February 8th 2014
The climate, not the weather

In the month of my eighty-first birthday (please don't bother, but thanks anyway) it rather seems that the future has arrived without waiting till I've gone. How much longer can my polytunnel go on bucking on its arches like a frightened horse without taking to the sky or tearing itself into shreds – this my plastic palace, seat of music and meditation, my place of trust in tomorrow and the springing of green leaves? How long before the twenty-year-old greenhouse (built with concrete pillars, half-sunk into the ground, buttressed against the house and given a sheltering hedge of its own) finally succumbs in a squall of shattering glass? What do we do with all the bits? But that is to anticipate.

Unlike the unfortunate people on the western and southern estuaries, we are lucky to live high on a hillside and can watch with simple awe as the tide sweeps into the freshwater fen behind the dunes. In appropriate lulls, well anoraked, I go for my daily march. The boreen is lined with flailing briars, never so blackly and thornily stripped of leaves. I look in vain among the mosses and ferns for the first bright glint of lesser celandine, but it needs the sun, the sun! And don't tell me about all your early daffodils: a hungry badger has found my best bulbs and ploughed them up to eat.

Thus my February blues, unleavened, as I write, by any "pet" day of gilded calm.

Quite often, given the usual lead time of this column, just discussing the weather is enough to change it by the day my words appear: I sometimes feel I should apologise. But we are now talking about climate, not weather, and this winter has fulfilled – even, indeed, excelled – the dire promises of the modellers. Hurricane gusts, twenty -metre waves, surging tides: it's all happening.

In response from the human world, of course, nothing commensurate is happening. It probably never will until, cataclysm piling on disaster, governments are besieged by a panicked populace – all, by that time, too late and to no purpose.

Most people now, even in the biblically deluded, anti-science strata of the US, accept that climate is changing. But far too many still hold, irrationally, that we had nothing to do with it. In the meantime a warming of two degrees, once felt to be the tolerable limit, has slipped forward half a century. Now the heat is being turned up; four degrees by the end of the century is the outcome advanced in the latest report to the World Bank.

For the slow awakening of popular knowledge, the media have much to regret. News and comment thrive by confrontation, so any assertion with dramatic significance must immediately be matched with someone to deny it. Counterarguments are offered in challenging tones by presenters pleading "balance".

Thus a worldwide scientific consensus has had to struggle with the appearance of debate where none should now exist. On the dangers of our present path, now rehearsed in one "extreme" weather episode after another, no credible room remains for denial. (For further insight and instruction, go to realclimate.org, a website on the sensible side of science.)

Given all that, how does an eighty-one-year-old with no faith in an afterlife keep his sense of humour? With some desperation at times and perhaps especially in February with another storm due. It is sad to conceive of a west of Ireland whose more exposed coasts could become virtually depopulated, at least in winter, not so much because of storm damage – farms and sheep will adapt – as because of the stress of unrelenting wind and rain. Perhaps the people of Shetland or the Faroes are made of sterner stuff, or don't have polytunnels and greenhouses.

That thought took me, of course, straight to Google, and discovery of the

Shetland invention of the "polycrub", a polytunnel made by recycling old salmon cage pipe (of which there now is a lot to spare, apparently), its arches covered with stormproof twin-wall polycarbonate.

The Northmavine community – Shetland is good at community action – made land available and used money from Scotland's Climate Challenge Fund to build twelve sturdy polytunnels to grow fruit and veg. Even redundant salmon cage walkways have been rescued by the tonne to serve between the beds. Connacht, perhaps, please copy.

So it's not just the jokes that keep me going but a restless curiosity about the natural world and the human role within it, at once so clever and creative, so greedy and self-deceiving.

I would love to come back at the end of the century to see how it all works out: whether migrants from Africa have fetched up in Thallabawn, whether the rich have built their new forts in Greenland. But then, when I was small, 2014 belonged on comic book covers, with everyone in flying cars, zooming between the skyscrapers.

Back, next week, to the world as we thought we knew it.

April 26th 2014
Our big white willow

A blaze of golden yellow halfway down the garden proclaims an invader to our small estate, where a self-sown goat willow, Salix caprea, offers glorious catkins to the spring.

Others of its kind light up my morning march, leaning from the banks of streams beyond the snowy sparkle of whitethorn.

These are all male willow catkins, despite the feminine flourish of the pollen: a twig or two, bracing narcissi in a vase, spread the table with gold dust.

The new trespasser more than earns its niche. But the acre we came to had a willow of its own, couched in the hollow where the hill stream cuts through beside the house.

The tree is now quite huge, leaning big, mossy elbows on the opposite bank of the stream. In summer its canopy blots out the mountain from our windows; in winter it cradles the summit and the rise of the moon.

Being so big, it is probably some class of white willow, Salix alba. I am allowed to be that vague, as the hybridisation of willows in Ireland is botanically remarkable. The old Webb's An Irish Flora, everyday bible of Irish botanists, detailed fifteen species, most of them native to the island but some half-dozen introduced.

The new edition, updated in 2012, adds no more species, but has plenty to say about how difficult it has become to tell one willow from another. John Parnell and Tom Curtis write that eighteen hybrids have now been recorded in Ireland, with probably more to come.

Even triple hybrids are known, "but it is even more difficult to determine their parentage".

Our big white willow should have leaves made silvery green by a coating of silky white hairs. I remember a breathtaking tree of such pure heritage beside a river in Leitrim, a county made especially beautiful by its riparian willows in spring. Our tree's leaves are bald and dull, but, hybrid or no, it has every ambition to spread its genes. Its winged seeds will float in a feathery blizzard for days and then spring up from every outdoor flower pot or root stubbornly into crevices in paths or walls.

The Salicaceae evolved for the cool moist soils of the northern hemisphere, into the High Arctic, where I walked on its catkins in a long-past July.

In Ireland it was one of the first plants to colonise the postglacial tundra; it survives in prostrate form now on coastal mountainsides and in the hollows of dunes.

The late, great naturalist Frank Mitchell wrote of kneeling at a seam of silt at Ashleam Bay, in Achill, to pick out 5,000 little fossilised leaves for radiocarbon dating – it was 11,000 years since they grew.

The native species accumulated by this island (goat, grey, bay, eared, purple, sally are the commonest) enriched our early ecosystems through their roots, stabilising the banks of streams (and thus making holts for otters and hideaways for fish), and through their insect populations – perhaps 250 species – and the birds that feed on them.

For people it was their infinite suppleness and durability that brought the sallies to so many farmsteads. (Just push a live stick two-thirds deep into a soggy spot, and within a few years, a bush!) Along with the native sally came others from Britain: osier, crack willow, even the white willow that grew into our big tree.

They were all planted for their use in thatching, wattle-walling and every kind of basket, from the potato platter to the creel of bog and currach.

Today, willow achieves value for its potential in "bioenergy", rivalling miscanthus grass as a perennial crop and coppiced every three years for woodchip boilers. There's a grant of up to €1,300 per hectare towards the cost of establishing the plantation, and a whole range of new willow varieties has been developed for the industry.

"Genetic improvement" of willows for biomass, breeding for pest resistance and to suit a wider range of environments and future climates, has been pursued in Sweden and the UK for decades.

More than twenty new species now include "exotic equivalents" of the goat willow and the tall osier, Salix viminalis, common on Irish roadsides and riverbanks, and each year sees another one or two new varieties.

Teagasc has published an identification guide to the willows now on offer, with uplifting names like Beagle, Endeavour, Resolution, Advance, Endurance. It specifies their promised yields, calorific value, shoots per stool and stem thickness at a metre tall. Endeavour, it persuades, is denser, drier and has the most thermal calories of all, so that its wood chips will take up less storage space and burn for longer.

What all this will do for telling apart the wayside willows of the future I have no idea.

May 3rd 2014

Screaming swifts: the sound of summer

I miss the coming of city swifts – the change in the sky from one day to the next. In my rooftop bachelor pad in Ballsbridge, circa 1965, I enjoyed the sudden swirl of fresh life above the chimneys, the space-carving arcs of flight, each with its gliding cursor of dark wings. Occasionally, when the traffic eased, I could even hear them calling – screaming, if you like.

Most Dubliners, heads bent as they hurry or cocked to a mobile, may take longer to register the arrival, in the next few days, of the last spring migrants from Africa. In the Georgian, horse-drawn city, swifts could scarcely be ignored as they swooped down and dashed through the streets to feast on a haze of golden dung flies, sometimes knocking off hats as they flew.

They were nesting, two or three pairs at a time, in crevices beneath the window sills of red-brick houses, also in their eaves and soffit boards, and in the more natural crannies of cliffs at Howth and Bray Head. In today's cities of concrete and glass there are few such accommodating apertures, and a European effort has sprung up to check the global decline of Apus apus, at least as an urban visitor.

In Ireland this has been led by amateur enthusiasts in the North (their website is at saveourswifts.co.uk) who have established swift nesting colonies on their houses. Helped by ornithologists in the Republic, they promote the use of "swift bricks" – hollow bricks made of woodcrete. Like garden tit boxes or bat boxes, these provide new breeding posts at a growing number of modern rooflines around the country.

Some are fitted to plant rooms on top of Dublin's civic offices (viewable from Ormond Quay). To quote from last month's international conference on swifts in Cambridge in England, "Screaming swifts are the sound of summer from Dublin to Beijing." But they are by no means a pleasure exclusive to big cities, and the conference welcomed Lynda Huxley of Galway-Mayo Institute of Technology in Castlebar.

She heads the college's "green campus" committee, which, two years ago, installed a dozen nest boxes under the eaves of the refurbished old psychiatric hospital. Last year swifts were filmed exploring the boxes and even bringing nesting material into them.

This year infrared cameras are installed in all of them, and events in the four most active will be streamed live on the institute's home page (gmit.ie) – the only such peep show in Ireland.

It's seventy-odd years since the British ornithologist David Lack persuaded swifts to exchange nesting space on ledges high in a tower of Oxford University Museum of Natural History for a set of nesting boxes built in the same space. As the birds settled to their annual visits, the backs of the boxes were replaced by glass. Summer after summer, Lack and his wife perched under the tiles, in the dark, to watch – and even, lifting the lid, to take out eggs and young for weighing and measuring.

The birds seemed not to mind this intrusion from the rear, while fighting bitterly any incoming swift attempting dispossession.

They could be locked in violent breast to breast battle in the close space for hours – "it looks horrid," wrote Lack – so the Castlebar video may occasionally be well up to television drama. And the nestlings, too, were "hideous" – quite naked and pot-bellied. But, as Lack said, "this distorted monster is really a miracle of adaptation", storing fat for its eventual, unaided launch into a most uncertain air.

The consensus that swifts spend nine months of their year in the sky, touching down only to breed their young in a hole, is comparatively new. It's true that Gilbert White of Selborne, in the 1790s, accurately described their aerial mating. ("Both of them sink down together for many fathoms with a loud piercing shriek.") And many modern scientists were long convinced that swifts also did their sleeping on the wing.

But it was the mid-twentieth century before respected observers felt like stating it as fact.

David Lack, watching swifts rising at dusk and disappearing out over the sea, decided "the mystery of where migrating swifts spend the night has been solved. They go up into the sky." Speculating on their "catnaps" to avoid bumping into each other, he anticipated research on the widespread avian ability to sleep with one eye and half the brain open.

The idea that swifts ascend specifically to sleep may, however, need modification.

Dutch scientists, using weather radar to track swift altitudes, found them ascending up to 2,500 metres at twilight, but doing it again at dawn. Among the reasons, they thought, could be to get a better view of where they were going, and of the kind of weather ahead. One presumes that they come down in between.

May 17ᵗʰ 2014

The special Irish stoat

Stoats are our now-and-then neighbours, glimpsed in ripples across the road or at frozen moments on top of a wall. I have watched one swimming in a pool on the shore and another at full stretch after rabbits on the duach. In a recent hard winter we had some dainty close-ups through the kitchen window, as one fed from bird crumbs outside on the sill.

Stoats don't really care if we're looking or not; they're beautiful, single-minded hunters. Once, in a low-budget winter in Connemara, I took a rabbit off a stoat when they tumbled together at my feet on a bog road, and it followed me along the walls all the way home. Its angry vibes pierced my back, for, as Giraldus Cambrensis wrote in the twelfth century, the stoat can be "vindictive and relentless in its wrath".

Stoats have been around so long in Ireland that you'd think there's nothing left to know about them, apart from not being the "weasels" that rural Ireland commonly supposed. But even zoologists who have made a special study of them are fascinated by all the questions that remain. Dr Paddy Sleeman of University College Cork, for example, who wrote a book about them, says that there are "huge gaps in our knowledge".

Some of the gaps are simple, as in how many Mustela erminea hibernica the Irish countryside supports. There has been an estimate of 160,000, but that was just a guess based on British figures.

The maps of the ongoing Irish Mammal Atlas show big regional differences between sightings prior to 2010 and those reported since then. But you have to be careful in drawing conclusions.

Perhaps Northern Ireland has, indeed, lost an awful lot of stoats just lately, as intensive farming and rodent control have reduced the animals' food supply – or perhaps just fewer people have been looking there than in the Republic. There's a big splash of new records around Galway and Waterford, for example, because of important new surveys to measure the stoats' presence.

In Galway, Vincent Wildlife Trust, in partnership with ecologists at NUI Galway, set 600 small plastic tubes, lined with dabs of glue and baited with rabbit meat, along the hedgerows and stone walls of the county. When the DNA of pulled-off hairs was analysed at Waterford Institute of Technology almost half the locations proved positive for stoat.

A further trial around Waterford shows stoats at a third of sites. Along with sightings from wildlife wardens, forestry workers and the public, a more accurate mapping and population estimate should result.

What's so special about the Irish stoat is the hibernica at the end of its name and the history and physical differences that go with it. It is a distinct and separate Irish subspecies of the European stoat, certainly here before the last ice age and again about 11,000 years ago. (We know this from fossil bones in Co Cork caves.)

As a rare link to an ancient ecosystem, it is adapted to the cold but not to sitting snow, which is why it doesn't need to go white (ermine) in winter. This may also link to the wavy line between the brown back and white belly, shown in most of our stoats, so different from the straight line of stoats in the rest of Europe.

Size also matters – sometimes rather oddly, as in that stoats in the north of Ireland are smaller than those in the south. Paddy Sleeman thinks this might be because southern stoats have rabbits to eat much earlier than those in the north.

But diet has often raised questions about the stoat's survival. What on earth did they eat after the ice ages when the lemmings were gone? And what was around in postglacial Ireland: were stoats then fish-eating, coastal dwellers, as some sightings, even now, suggest?

Today they climb trees, after birds, and burrow into rubbish dumps, after rats, but exactly what they eat becomes important again as new small mammal species – bank vole and greater white-toothed shrew – spread across Ireland to offer potential new prey, or reduce and outcompete the native shrews and field mice. As stoat casualties mount on the roads, more stomachs will find their way to the relevant laboratories.

Meanwhile, the Irish mustelid family has offered interesting grist to evolutionary biologists studying the way size is graded between species in the group – say, from stoat to mink to pine marten, to otter and then to badger. It seems that the males of each species are smaller than the females of the next larger species.

There's so much still to know.

July 5th 2014

Jobs for jellyfish

Those remarkable calms, mirroring the sky in the sea and stroking the coasts with mere wavelets and ripples, have been setting the ocean's drifters ashore, each on its own gentle rush of bubbles. Some, like the many barrel jellyfish delivered to the south coast, are among the biggest of their kind. But with them have come a first few of some of the smallest of drifting medusae and actually, despite appearances, not true jellyfish at all.

Velella velella, the by-the-wind sailor, arrives on our Atlantic beaches at almost any time of year and in greatly varying numbers – sometimes in glittering millions, as in 1992. Late that July they came ashore almost simultaneously along a 400-kilometre stretch, from Cork to Mayo. Tens of thousands choked rock pools in Connemara and more edged the tide in continuous ribbons.

Here at Thallabawn I gathered hundreds, some the size of my palm, others just a few centimetres across.

They carried shreds of blue jelly from their float, some still with the fringe of stubby feeding tentacles. But the jelly dries out rapidly on the beach, leaving only the rainbowed, oval disc embedded in its surface and the small, transparent triangular flap, like cellophane, set upright and diagonally across it. These are more durable structures, like bits of plastic, and, bleached by the sun, are often what the holiday beachcomber stoops for and puzzles over.

I had a reason for gathering so many from the strand. The little sail is made to catch the ocean's surface wind and move the animal on to fresh sources of planktonic food. It is found across all the big oceans and everywhere shares a variation. On some discs, the sail is set NW-SE; on others, NE-SW. In the same wind, one animal will sail leftwards, the other to the right, either veering as much as sixty degrees away from the wind's direction.

This engineering scatters the species widely, being mixed as larvae (or so it is hypothesised) in the middle of the ocean. In the northern Atlantic, where winds twist eastwards in rotation of Earth's atmosphere, it is most often the left-sailing Velella that end up on our beaches. Of my discs, 228 were left-sailers and forty-two were right-sailers, which seemed to bear this out.

The exact biological identity of Velella has been slow to emerge: if not a true jellyfish, then what sort of hydrozoan? Its sail suggested an affinity with the big Portuguese man-o-war, travelling beneath an inflatable crest. But that is a colonial creature, each component with a different function.

Velella is an individual animal and actually, it seems, an upside-down and floating variation among the hydroids, a class of organisms more usually moored to the sea floor.

Velella sinks deeply in mid-ocean to reproduce, but never reaches the bottom.

As jellyfish and their kin move up the research agenda, their role in the global ecosystem is becoming clearer. A recent University College Cork project, led by Dr Tom Doyle, studied the Velella abundant in the Celtic Sea. His team found rafts of floating seaweed rounded up by currents and wind and with them lots of Velella feeding on sea life that gathers under the weed – little fish, fish eggs and zooplankton. As predators, they thus become important in carbon cycling, and, in finally drifting ashore to rot, sometimes in masses, bringing some of the open ocean's production to nourish the edge of the land.

Velella itself feeds other creatures, among them the Janthina drifting sea snail. This hangs below a raft of bubbles that it creates by trapping the wind in little blisters of mucus. I am fascinated by its lifestyle – not least the incredible workings of chance that bring drifting predator and prey together.

Janthina sometimes arrives on the west coast together with the stranded jellies, its fragile and beautiful violet shell a beachcomber's prize.

From one particular cove of the wild western shore comes a new and remarkable labour of love in a book called Seasons, Species & Patterns of a North East Atlantic Rocky Shore, by Carmel Madigan.

The cool title speaks for five years of close study, together with much fine and gloriously colourful photography, of life between the tides at rocky Ross Beach, beside Loop Head in Co Clare.

Madigan, with long family history on this shore, is a professional artist who runs summer hedge schools on nature. Her new book, initially inspired by her schoolboy son James, also plumbs the harshest of seasons and winter storms to trace changes and events among the creatures of the sharp-edged rock pools and weed-hung gullies.

Full of the shared excitement of the project and supported by sound research, it makes a beautiful and enlightening companion for any holiday by the Atlantic. It is also, while warmly individual, a valuable work of field observation for any student of the shore.

August 2nd 2014
An invisible chorus above my window

We needed a few bright logs from the woodshed to take the bleak look off the cold summer stove.

Would the swallows mind? They've had the shed to themselves these past few weeks, plastering this year's nest to a roof beam and swooping in and out to attend their brood. They've been master and mistress of the way to the gate, swishing back and forth from dawn to dusk to scythe invisible midges.

With a muttered "Never mind me" I stooped to find a likely grip on timber, whereupon a dark explosion erupted above my head. The fledglings fanned out in panic, then wheeled above the trees in what I fondly choose to think was their first flight.

There were now too many swallows carving the air to be sure how many swallows there were. Eventually the young ones settled, perching in a row on the roof gutter above my bedroom window: an invisible chorus of twittering, rising and falling between parental feeds. I crept out to count and scored four before they flew. There might have been three, the modest beginners' brood, or up to half a dozen. Brood size is partly matched to insect abundance: swallow species in Europe lay more eggs than those in the tropics, where shorter summer days give fewer feeding hours.

But I have been learning about another, subtle organ of control: the brood patch.

Kitchen-window birdwatchers will have noticed, perhaps, a cleft in the breast feathers of, say, a motherly thrush, out taking a break on a branch – may know, indeed, that it marks the patch of bare skin that keeps the eggs warm beneath her in the nest.

That it does much more is explored in the chapter on touch in Tim Birkhead's excellent book Bird Sense (Bloomsbury, 2012).

The egg is warmed by the flow of blood to the skin, and this is under the bird's regulation. But contact between egg and brood patch also triggers the release of the hormone prolactin from the pituitary gland beneath her brain, and this, in turn, keeps her incubating until her clutch of eggs is completed.

What happens if the eggs are removed can be remarkable and was first tested in an experiment by the English naturalist Martin Lister as long ago as the 1670s. As a swallow laid her eggs, Lister removed them one after another, whereupon the bird continued to lay no fewer than nineteen before stopping.

There have been other such heartless if illuminating interventions: the sparrow that laid fifty eggs instead of the usual four or five, and an American northern flicker that reached seventy-one over seventy-three days. But some birds – the lapwing is one – are immune to such interference and just lay the number of eggs their species is used to. Ornithologists now divide birds into determinate and indeterminate egg-layers, but they still don't know the rationale.

The day of the young swallows seemed to fill the garden with little birds: great tits perched in series up a thistle; blue tits tapping our windows for spiders; willow warblers tiptoeing over the fronds of a conifer.

This was all very delightful but could not last. Young birds succumb to the wanderlust that science calls dispersal, while the older ones hide in the shadows to change their feathers for the winter. August brings to the garden a different mood and, without the promptings of territory or hunger, a slowly relaxing silence.

All birds moult, but in different ways. Small birds can't afford to lose their speed and flight power. They change their feathers a few at a time, new ones pushing the old ones out. The starling, for example, started shedding its main flight feathers in late June, and the total replacement of its plumage takes about 100 days. The young birds in the little summer flocks, zooming around the hillside in quite alarming, hedge-hopping flight, seem too dark to be starlings at all. But by springtime the tips of their feathers will have worn away, leaving the sleek, iridescent, bright-speckled starlings that we know.

Young blackbirds, too, have begun to moult into adult plumage, changing all their feathers except those of the tail and some in the wings. The results can confuse the human eye, some of the males almost as black and glossy as their fathers, others, in this first year, almost as brown as their mothers. Adult blackbirds, wandering out on the lawn with a moult half-complete, can look distinctly scruffy and declasse and fleetingly uncertain of their sex.

I end with how it works for our barnacle geese in Greenland. When the chicks are born and coaxed to whirr down from the cliffs, the family groups march across the tundra to the nearest big lake. There, the parents drop their primary flight feathers.

While new ones grow, any glimpse of a fox sends the flock out into the middle, where they float together safely in a raft of black and silver.

August 30th 2014

The rise of peregrines

The wind above the cliffs of Dubhoileán Mór was dishevelling even for a peregrine, tugging so fiercely at the thatch of his wings that the usual trim anchor of the falcon's silhouette was split into a fistful of knives.

He hung at perhaps ten metres up from the sea pink cushions where I lay, ogling him through binoculars, and he screamed at me angrily for half an hour. This was his place in the sky, it seemed, for he would sweep away and return to it exactly, hovering like a weathervane or a compass needle.

So this was one encounter with a peregrine that carried the full, wild weight of its presence. Dubhoileán Mór – Duvillaun More in English – is an island between the north cliffs of Achill and the tip of Iniskea, where the bothy ruins are felted with grey-green lichens and many of its rabbits are unexpectedly black. I was there with David Cabot to film the autumnal grey seals and their pups, but it is the falcon that has stayed in mind.

Half a century after their DDT disaster, peregrine falcons are in full recovery, but they follow somewhat different lifestyles on Ireland's opposite coasts.

In the west they breed on the cliffs of islands and mountains, preying on nesting seabirds and those of the farmland valleys.

In winter they hunt the sandy shores and estuaries for migrant waders. They have no particular human enemies beyond occasional thieves of their young and eggs for black-market falconry, and their most violent quarrels are with ravens.

On the eastern littoral of Ireland, where high, safe places are scarcer, every other quarry has had a place in the falcons' recovery.

Urban peregrines find security on the ledges of tall office blocks, churches and industrial constructions. And while winter takes them to the great bird flocks of the Irish Sea bays, their prey in the breeding season has a very different flavour.

Peregrines are increasing in most European cities, but studies of food they take to their chicks are rare. One by the University of Bristol analysed the daily prey of city peregrines in southwestern England, in Bristol, Bath and Exeter. Along with starlings and jackdaws, migrant birds were hunted at night. But pigeons formed about forty per cent of the diet in the breeding season.

Pigeons and doves are a leading food for peregrines wherever they live worldwide. Unfortunately, many of the pigeons based in cities are not wild at all but the property of passionate people who breed them for their special beauty (as in the traditional Limerick tumbler) or, more relevantly, to compete in races from distant points to test the birds' exceptional homing instincts.

Long-distance pigeon racing is now an international enthusiasm, and most developed countries have racing unions. Last month some 26,000 pigeons were released in a marathon race from Barcelona, crossing the Pyrenees to reach home lofts in the UK, Belgium and the Netherlands. In China, one race challenges pigeons with flights of more than 1,900 kilometres, incredible tests of both navigation and sheer survival.

In Ireland, races are much shorter, from release in Rosslare to home lofts in Dublin and Belfast. Ambushes by east-coast peregrines are the owners' biggest fear, as even a failed attack can send a highly valued pigeon fleeing off course – minus, perhaps, a few tail feathers – to end up in someone's garden on the other side of Ireland. (And, no, the owner will not want it back.) In the UK, with some 60,000 pigeon owners, a highly organised lobby, the Raptor Alliance, has been seeking legal recognition of the birds as "livestock" deserving protection from predators in wildlife legislation. A poisoning of peregrines in Wales in 2012 brought police raids on the homes of four pigeon fanciers.

In Ireland, recourse to darker direct action has been apparent for twenty years, and also in recent shootings and poisonings.

An enlightening study of the fortunes of peregrines breeding on the inland and coastal cliffs of southeast Ireland from 1981 to 2001 was undertaken by Dr Declan McGrath of Waterford Institute of Technology and published in the Irish Naturalists' Journal in 2002. An early increase, to eleven breeding pairs in 1991, he wrote, "may have been facilitated by an enhanced food supply provided by passing pigeons".

A marked decline in breeding success thereafter, achieved by seven pairs, was matched to "intentional disturbance at many of the accessible coastal eyries" and the appearance of poisoned pigeon carcasses tied to cliff-top fence posts. McGrath concluded that the peregrine population of the southeast "is now comparable to that recorded there at the turn of the century and is constrained...by deliberate persecution".

In 1900, as Robert Ussher and Richard Warren recorded, almost all the eagles had been exterminated from Ireland, but the peregrine "fairly holds its own wherever cliffs afford it suitable haunts".

September 13th 2014
What's changed in all these years?

When you're my age, hedges grow as fast as time is passing: insidiously and far too quickly, with Sunday twice a week. There also comes a point when wielding the hedge cutter at all, never mind at shoulder height, joins the growing list of things best left to others.

Thus, as summer passed, the fuchsia outside my workroom window added a metre to its height, its new facade of crimson bells, attended by foraging bumblebees, helping to make up for the loss of the world outside.

By the time a good neighbour, his ladder and a dry day came together I had grown used to a life doubly screened, by the fleeting images of broadband and by the real wall of leaves beyond.

And then, with a whirr (lots of whirrs), the vista was restored: hillside, shore, sea, islands, more sea, a final, soft-edged horizon some fifty kilometres away. I thought of our Finnish writer friends whose visits were celebrations of not looking out into dark pine forest.

Now, like Riittta and Olli, I repossess a distance that seems to fill the soul.

At left a slow uncurling of surf at a corner of the strand, then a long ridge of grassy dunes and a sort of lost valley of sand inside, before the fields begin. A long march of poles through the sheep to the rise of the hill and another row of them, higher up, along the road – seventeen poles on the left, a dozen on the right where the hawthorn in the hedge interrupts.

That's ESB to seaward and Eircom mainly on the ditch, the gales testing their matchstick verticals in a landscape bowing to the cloud theatre of the sky.

The hawthorn bush is reaching for the eaves, and bracken cloaks more and more of the rough pasture beyond. What else has changed in all these years? At the top of the hill two new holiday houses replace the thatched hump of Maggie's cottage, with its bog-deal props and purlins, its outshot bed, the close web of old stone walls. The new houses are decently "vernacular" and painted a neighbourly white. Just out of sight starts the brave new world of glass walls and telescopes on tripods.

Out at sea, left to right: Inishbofin, Inishturk, Caher Island, with a few low, dark islets in between, each skirted with foam.

When, last summer, young friends sailed back from New Zealand, the solitary white fleck of our first glimpse of their yacht made the empty ocean seem ten times its size. How different will it look, I wonder, if big new salmon farms draw circles on the deeps behind the islands? Busier, that's for sure.

Move fish farms offshore – the farther the better. More vigorous waves in deeper water bubbling with oxygen make salmon use their muscles, swimming more strongly around and around to build firmer, tastier flesh. Stronger currents flush through the cages and sweep the seabed of waste food and life-smothering excrement. Parasitic sea lice are held far from the migrant paths of our last few native salmon and sea trout.

Those, anyway, are the hopes of An Bord Iascaigh Mhara.

Farther out, on the other hand, means much rougher sea, even more so in the brand of storms promised by climate change. In last February's tempests, in Bantry Bay, one cage was smashed into another and upended, spilling 230,000 fish into unaccustomed freedom. Nor is forty metres of water – the ideal depth – any shield against poisonous algal blooms and toxic jellyfish shredding through the mesh.

In the lee of Clare Island, around the corner in Clew Bay, a pioneer farm in deeper mooring has suffered its share of amoebic gill disease, a new plague of farmed salmon stemming from assaults by malevolent algae and the wrong sort of zooplankton. The industry's engineers are working on technology to sink cages to the seabed for safety, ahead of hurricanes, swarms of jellyfish and toxic blooms, all to be signalled by satellite spies in the sky.

Bord Iascaigh Mhara has been plumbing sheltered depths off the west for a decade. Of two new Mayo prospects, the most immediately probable is a farm rearing 3,500 tonnes of salmon (not the rumoured 5,000 tonnes concerning some islanders) and anchored two and a half kilometres southeast of Inishturk, a good binocular spot in the middle of my window.

A second site, with no plans in prospect yet (according to Bord Iascaigh Mhara) is east of Inishbofin, near the islet of Lecky Rocks. A few fierce westerlies will deliver a whole new beachcombers' harvest of buckets, ropes and bits of net on our strand, but I doubt I shall be first on the tideline.